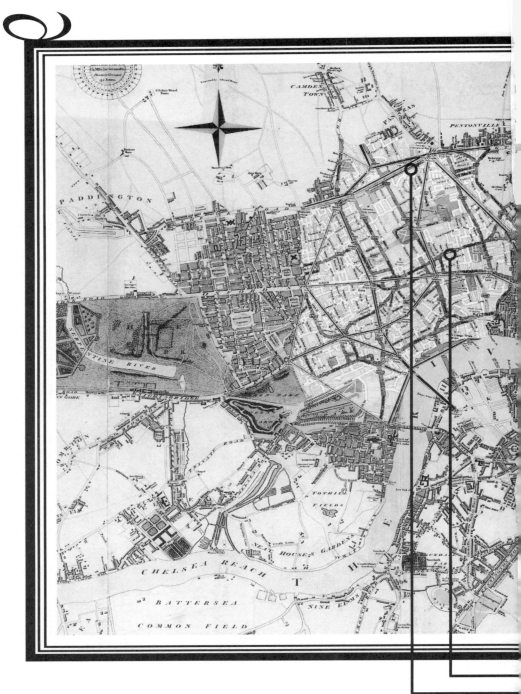

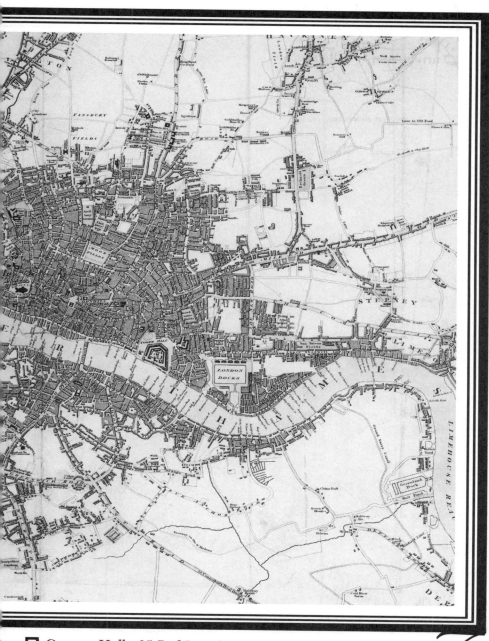

Conway Hall - 25 Red Lion Square - London
Camden Centre - Bidborough Street - London (Friday evening-Opening Gala party)

printed in an
edition of
777

Equinox 2009

TABLE OF CONTENTS

CREDITS

Festival Directors – Raymond Salvatore Harmon
Simon Kane
Andrew Hartwell

Catalogue Editor – RS Harmon
Associate Editor – Mark Pilkington

Layout & Design – RS Harmon
Proof Reader – Frances Morgan

Catalog contributors: Carl Abrahamsonn, David Beth, Peter
Christopherson, Erik Davis, Orryelle Defenestrate-Bascule,
Paul Devereux, Phil Farber, Stephen Grasso, Andrew Hartwell,
Paola Igliori, Alan Moore, Ralph Metzner, Mark Pilkington, Jack
Sargeant, Robert Wallis, Matthew Wiley, Z'EV, John Zorn.

Festival House Manager – Elizabeth Philips
Festival Archivist – Todd Andrew Carter

ISBN : 978-1-907222-00-9
Published by Strange Atractor Press,
BM SAP, London WC1N 3XX, UK.
www.strangeattractor.co.uk

Printed by Cromwell Press Group, Trowbridge, Wiltshire

The Equinox Festival is a work of love. We believe that it is important
that this festival occur, and to that end we are grateful for the help and
support of everyone who has made the event possible. Thank you.

MAIN SPONSORS

SPONSORS & PARTNERS

VENUES + INFO

Conway Hall - 25 Red Lion Square - London

Opened in 1929 Conway Hall is the home of the South Place Ethical Society, the oldest surviving free thought organisation in the world. A landmark of London's independent intellectual, political and cultural life, Conway Hall is renowned as a hub for free speech and progressive thought.

In recent years it has hosted events ranging from magickal conferences to talks by authors Salman Rushdie and Will Self and is equally well-known as a centre for contemporary classical and experimental music festivals.

Camden Centre - Bidborough Street - London

The Camden Centre was designed by AJ Thomas, a former assistant of Edwin Lutyens, whose classical influence pervades the building. Thomas designed several housing schemes for St Pancras Borough Council from 1924 onwards. It features an extensive amount of architectural detail, including art-deco ornamentation and original lighting fixtures.

London's oldest remaining civic centre, The Camden Centre has played host to talks and performance by a wide range of spectacular guests, including Terence McKenna and Hugo Chavez.

List of plates/images

All article closing graphics courtesy Barry William Hale.

Welcome

The Equinox Working

Sometime during the late 20th century, the science of curating became an artform. Rather than using tools like painting and sculpting the curator-as-artist creates form with the works of others. The curator's palette is shaded with personalities and ideals, its colours provided by the vast array of individuals creating work. The curator draws together all these emotions, colours, and ideas and gives them structure; shaping this multiplicity of expression and building with it a great temple in which a scared ritual must occur.

Much in the way that a curator collects artists over time, the journeyer must prepare, sometimes a year in advance, in order to achieve his goals. The shaman must alter his diet, limit his social interaction and retune his mind through meditation and modification. He must seek out specific ingredients and often employ other individuals to help them in his task.

Like the shaman the curator must prepare, must plan, discuss and consider the variables far in advance of the actual undertaking.

One must choose the dates for their event and consider the preparations in store. The form of the exhibition becomes the prepatory ritual for the theatre of the mind.

Thus the gallery has become the temple, the hallowed halls of the white cube have become the shelter to that form which seeks illumination, that curiosity which explores being, that expression of self which is both creation and creator.

In bringing together this festival we have chosen only that which made itself whole in the tapestry. We have moved and ordered the collective ideas so that they may reflect on one another, the facets of a jewel that become the structure of its beauty.

Only when one stands away from the three days of the Equinox Festival and considers the overall form of its aesthetics can its real mission be understood. For its task is not just to bring the world an illuminating week's end with a collection of astounding minds and creative souls. It is to bring these very souls into contact with one another in the hope that new and inspiring ideas will develop forth from the occasion; to inseminate the broadest understanding of spiritual self expression and to celebrate the birth of new explorations of being, while we reflect on the tools of the past.

I call upon all of you, participants in this great undertaking, to look to one another, to collaborate and to exchange ideas. To build new forms from familiar shapes and to create anew the experience that is becoming.

- Raymond Salvatore Harmon
Walpurgisnacht, 2009

s a bookish only child with a growing obsession with Iron Maiden, studying for an early O-Level in Religious Education was always going to prove to be an enlightening pursuit. I remember being amazed at how there were so many biblical references and names I recognised from the music I listened to, and how so much of the contents of our course seemed contradictory, fragmented and alien. In my school you took R.E. as an easy qualification: the students would breeze through the course as they were all good Christian souls and knew the material, so went the thinking. It was, however, the kind of course where you were supposed to toe the line, and not ask awkward questions. Even then it was clearly strange to be taught a medieval take on an earlier creation story while in the next lesson you'd be messing around with Bunsen burners and dissecting things. In many ways, the course had the opposite effect to that of a civilising force, making me question things more: if all this crazy stuff was in the Bible, what else was out there?

It also opened up for me the whole idea of belief, and the corresponding disbelief that goes hand in hand, the editing process which we use to construct our reality. To believe the Bible to be the word of God is one thing, but to ignore the freely available facts that it has been heavily edited, supplemented and mistranslated over hundreds of years in order to include and exclude people and cultures and support and destroy dynasties... Well, that's another thing altogether. I still struggle with this stuff: I can't understand how people willfully ignore facts to such a degree. That Christianity wholesale 'assimilated' the beliefs, gods, rituals and holy places of the cultures that preceeded it seems obvious nowadays, but clearly not to all. It's like there is a sham at the supposed heart of our society, and we're all supposed to play along.

It's this construction of a belief system and, therefore, day-to-day reality that I find so interesting, and that ties in so well with the 'occult'. Rarely does a word carry so many connotations whilst simultaneously covering such a broad area. Indeed the entire idea of anything being 'hidden' in the 21st Century is somewhat ridiculous. Want to read about Mithraic ritual while waiting for a bus? A quick Google from your phone and its all there for you. The bare crux of the matter to me seems to be that the Christians, the architects of power in Europe for the last 2000 years, have been making the whole thing up pretty much, so why do we need to follow any idea of there being a 'right way' to think about spiritual matters? I find the modern occult community refreshing in that it echoes this precisely. What works for you? What will help you achieve your goals? A little of this, a little of that, a truly modern and enlightened approach to the whole concept of belief, mind and spirit.

15

In helping to curate the Equinox Festival it has been amazing to see the breadth of the event open up before us. The fact that we have archaeo-acoustics and voudon under discussion at the same event, avant jazz next to acid folk. While discussing Equinox at a panel at the recent Roadburn festival in Holland, Steve Von Till of Neurosis spoke of the importance in these difficult and dark times of having a gathering, of having your people around you. I think Equinox Festival achieves that, and to be part of such a open-minded community, hungry for knowledge, is an amazing thing.

- Andrew Hartwell, May 2009

The *Method* of *Science*
The *Aim* of *Religion*

The Equinox Festival exists to provide a cross cultural platform for the exhibition of creative and innovative approaches to spiritual discovery. In providing such a platform our goal is:

To present, produce, and commission an annual media arts festival focused on theoretical and practical approaches to new forms of spiritual self expression.

To bring together a diverse group of leading academic theorists, historians and authors to converge for three days of cross-cultural discussions, debates and panels.

To offer an exciting look at the need for universal understanding and openness to new and historic approaches to perspectives on the experience of the beyond.

Interest in the beyond, its influence and power over our lives, is growing. Many of the practices of traditional experimental spiritual discovery are being looked at by an increasingly informed society. Our perspective on the state of human consciousness continues to increase in resolution as mankind moves forward in its spiritual evolution.

The contemporary ardour that has driven us to seek a more individual path toward spiritual discovery has existed for as long as the written word. As society evolves intellectually it seeks a path that may provide some insight into the broader situation of mankind's universal soul and a more individual approach to transcendental thinking.

17

It is the mission of the Equinox Festival to create a broader base of exposure for the examination of diverse forms of spiritual expression and to support active cultural diversity in all its forms. In doing so we bridge the gap between traditional and contemporary models of spiritual discovery at the frontiers of human knowledge, present academic approaches to historic ideologies, and cutting edge new media research into modern forms of transcendentalism.

A Festival of Scientific Illuminism

ARTICLES

Snakes & Ladders

Alan Moore

An oratory given at Conway Hall April 10th, 1999

e find ourselves in Red Lion Square, caught in the crosshairs of geography and time like sitting ducks, held always by the surface tension of the instant, by the sensory dazzle. Constant play of light, of neural ripples. Fluttering attention pinned to where and when and who we are. The honey-trap of our personal circumstance, of our familiar bodies restless in these chairs.

Our stories, our back-continuities that herded us down separate tracks towards this room, this mutual dark. Our various threads converging with the history of this location, braided into a macramé of event unique and unrepeatable in space-time. From this complex lace of moment, all our strands of individual information stretch away towards their different points of origin, through how we got here, winding back to where we're from.

In my case that would be Northampton, an unprepossessing blur on the M1, halfway to Birmingham.

At Naseby fields, outside the town, Oliver Cromwell closed the English Civil War in a display of brute Darwinian politic.

While near my house there stands the church where Francis Crick attended Sunday School before he went on to discover the dual helix that had really made all creatures great and small.

Crick was a pupil at Northampton Grammar School, next door to the asylum where John Clare was kept until his death. This was the place where Arthur Machen once performed before the inmates in a group of travelling players.

He remarked that those who drooled and cackled most amongst the audience turned out to be the warders and the local reverend, which possibly suggests the flavour of the place.

Where shall we begin? With Cromwell polishing his wart before the ride to Naseby?

Or with Francis Crick, half-listening to the story of the garden and the serpent, fidgeting on his hard bench at Sunday School?

Perhaps with Machen improvising madly in the madhouse grounds?

The Universe began according to 17th century Archbishop Ussher at nine in the morning on October 23rd, four thousand and four years B.C. though later evidence suggests things actually commenced fifteen to twenty billion years before.

This may have been with a spontaneous explosion from a point within a quantum vacuum, though more recent work describes our whole continuum as a 3D facet on a 4D crystal that's expanding rapidly within a 5D liquid.

Deeper quantum theory, meanwhile, has implied that our material universe is but the secondary product of a primal information: in the beginning was the Word. Our sun flamed into being some ten billion years ago, our planet some 5.5 billion years thereafter. It took some six hundred million years for scabs to form atop the blazing magma.

Within only fifty million years of this, life makes its debut. Eden was white-hot and radioactive. Eve and Adam were both anaerobic, breathed formaldehyde and cyanide.

Time passed, three thousand million years or so. Landscape and culture gradually emerged, burned in like details on an exposed Polaroid. This current spot becomes Red Lion Fields, seventeen-acre paddocks ranged about the Red Lion Inn.

The tavern's name, London's most common, has a touch of Alchemy surrounding it, retains a whiff of the alembic.

Red Lion Square itself is not set out till 1684. Nicholas Barbon is the man behind the scheme, strongly opposed by lawyers in the Gray's Inn Road, prototype eco-warriors who fear the Square will spoil their view. Pitched streetfights soon ensue between the barristers and builders, one side hurling writs, the other bricks.

The builders win. By 1698 the Square is complete, and will attract its own peculiar fauna:

Jonas Hanway, the first Englishman to carry an umbrella.

Muscular Christian F.D.Morris and his unintelligible sermons.

Silent movie queen Fay Compton.

Flickering visions. Faltering visionaries.

Back in 1661, some twenty years before the Square is conceived, it is decided that Oliver Cromwell should be tried condemned and executed for his crimes against the monarchy.

The fact that Cromwell has been in the ground since 1658 proves to be no impediment.

Dug up from his Westminster Abbey tomb along with remains of Ireton and Bradshaw, his confederates, the Lord Protector is dragged to Red Lion Fields and laid out overnight there at the Inn before the morning's trip to Tyburn for beheading and dismemberment.

Stretched on the beer-stained board through the long, creaking watches of the dark, the relic, three years dead, retains a stoic, puritan indifference.

Lank hair, fused now with the fraying scalp. Cobwebs of brain, disintegrating memories of smoke and insurrection crusted on the inner skull, which urban legend situates beneath an obelisk in the square, a brittle egg of spite and discontent.

Come the mid-nineteen-hundreds and you can't move for Pre-Raphaelites. Edward Burne-Jones and William Morris lodge at 17, Red Lion Square.

Morris knocks up some shelves to fill the new address, has a sawdust epiphany and ends up opening a furniture shop down the street at number 8.

John Ruskin often drops by for a chat on socialism or armchairs.

Five years before Burnes-Jones and Morris move to number 17, in 1851, the address is the residence of Dante Gabriel Rossetti. In the tenancy agreement it is stipulated that 'the models are under gentlemanly restraint as some artists are known to sacrifice the dignity of art to the baseness of passion'.

Reek of sex and turpentine.

Laudanum afternoons.

And somewhere in the future he digs his beloved Lizzie Siddall from her grave in order to retrieve the poems that he's buried with her.

These are not our promised resurrections.

Mortal doubt sets in.

Nearby at Gray's Inn, 4 Verulam Buildings in July 1899 Amelia, the first wife of Arthur Machen and his partner of twelve years succumbs to cancer.

Stuttering gaslight in the ochre smudge of their front bedroom. Amy's sudden burst of twilight language slurred by morphia. Her husband's tearful, helpless promises.

The works that he'll be known for are already at his heels.

The Great God Pan published 1894.

His most ingenious Chinese box, *The Three Imposters* published 1895.

Only two years ago, in 1897, he's wrapped up his latest novel; reached the summit of his Hill of Dreams.

Now, the descent. The downslopes of bereavement, melancholy a treacherous scree. One false step starts a landslide, thundering and incoherent in the breast.

The black seal is depression. We reel, punch-drunk, in the human ring.

Love and Death, working in a tag team, will undo us all.

We are insensate molecules, assembled from the accidental code engraved upon our genes.

Mud that sat up.

Chemicals mingle in our sediment and in their interactions and combustions we suppose we feel, suppose we love.

24

We reproduce, mathematically predictable as spores within a Petri dish.

We function briefly, then subside once more to the unknowing silt.

We are a blind contingency, an unimportant restlessness of dirt and yet Rossetti paints his dead Elizabeth, head tilted back on her impossibly slim throat, eyes closed against the golden light surrounding her.

Clay looks on clay and understands that it is beautiful.

Through us, the cosmos gazes in itself, adores itself, breaks its own heart.

Through us, matter stares slack-jawed at its own star-dusted countenance and knows, incredulously, that it knows.

And knows that it is universe.

Right from the start, existence was a worry. There have always been these long, nail-biting stretches of anxiety. After the fuss and fireball of that first Big Bang, there was no follow-up, just silent blackness lasting for millennia. The elements of substance were in place, but form would still take time. One flash, then that uncertain pause. The Universe as a substandard firework no-one dare approach. Was that it?

Protracted hush in that vast auditorium. Occasionally a cough of gamma rays. The tense, pre-curtain dark, extended for a thousand thousand centuries. First night nerves there in that first night. The quantum tingle of anticipation. Nobody knows what to expect at this unprecedented matinee. The author, if there is one, has no track record. The black decor yields no clue as to the drama yet to come, save to suggest it may not be a comedy. What if it's something difficult and Modern: Samuel Beckett with neutrinos? Meanwhile, the racket of existence tuning up.

A rhythm quartet of primeval powers: the weak force; gravity; electromagnetism; the strong force. Four titanic virtuosi, newly born and unrehearsed. There's no sheet-music, there's no set-list. Nothing for it now but improv jazz, although let's keep it tight. No room for solos.

If the start-conditions of the cosmos should be out by only half a beat, the weak force weaker or the strong force fractionally more butch, then matter will not fix and things will have no glue. No riff, just an undifferentiated background noise. The long, uneasy silence following the first event extends. The darkness shifts uncomfortably and then, above, just as we've given up on them, one at a time, the stars come on.

Imagine it!

The stage-lights go up slowly on this Theatre of Marvels. The breath-taking glamour of the painted background flats, their incandescent detail! Glimmering cloud-towers risen from the nebulae like fingers. Baby suns considering at their tips, along the diamond cuticle! Atomic decoration! The sheer gandeur of this set-design illuminates the whole amphitheatre that surrounds us. Seats of mass arranged in orbit rings and comets bustling like ushers with their torches in the aisles, alert for boisterous pulsars or for singularities furtively snogging in the blackout with their mouths wide open! All around, these shimmering furnitures in their Magellanic plush! Proscenium galaxies to frame the action! Chandeliers of constellation!

Planets cool about the fresh-lit suns, last minute touches to the scenery before the play commences. Where are the performers? Save for the occasional Greek chorus of a meteor storm, the spangled boards are empty. The harsh spotlight of the now awaits the opening act, awaits Life's debut, messy and unpolished, disappointingly under-attended. Many of our earliest creation stories, our first act scenarios, seem to give top billing to a snake. Sometimes it slides around a tree, or sometimes it coils the world about. Perhaps it has two heads, or is instead two separate serpents, winding up the shaft of a caduceus towards winged Godhead. DNA, the double helix, pulls itself together, accidentally from lifeless chemicals, while overhead the firmament flares into being.

In our every cell, furled at the nucleus, there is a ribbon two yards long and just ten atoms wide. Over a hundred million miles of DNA in every human individual, enough to wrap five million times around our world and make the Midgard serpend blush for shame, make even the Ourobouros worm swallow hard in disbelief. This snake-god, nucleotide, twice-twisted, scaled in adenine and cytosine, in thyamine and in guanine, is a one man show, will be the actors, props and setting, be the apple and the garden both. The player bides his time, awaits his entrance to a drum-roll of igniting binaries. This is the only dance in town, this anaconda tango, this slow spiral up through time from witless dirt to paramecium, from blind mechanic organism to awareness. There, below the birthing stars, life sways and improvises. Every poignant gesture drips with slapstick; pathos; an unbearably affecting bravery. To dare this stage, this huge and overwhelming venue. Squinting through the stellar footlights, hoping there's an audience, that there's someone there, but dancing anyway. But dancing anyway.

26

That's how it starts, in this primordial Odeon: the DNA, the Lifesnake, turning slowly underneath the nuclear spatter of the sky, the sequinned canopy. The serpent's magic number, 23, is mirrored in the number of paired chromosomes within the human recipe. This is the gorgeous worm described by Lady Frieda Harris in the luminous Thoth tarot she devised with Crowley.

Atu twenty-one, The Universe, the path that reaches up the quabalistic tree from Malkuth, the dominion of unknowing matter, up towards the higher plans of sentience arranged above. Upon the card the snake uncoils in languid ecstasy, surrounded by the elements and ringed by glittering Zodiac, but who's the woman that it dances with so erogenously? Who's that girl?

In those creation stories where the serpent gets a speaking part, a woman's usually involved. Take Eden. In the orthodoxy of the Golden Dawn it's said that Eve and Adam were at first hermaphrodite immortal beings, although possibly of limited potential.

With the Fall, for making love and also a fruit salad from the Tree of Good and Evil, they are cast out into the mortal world of sex and death, where they bear sons, a murderer and a victim. This is only comprehensible if Eve and Adam were amoebas, even to the detail of Eve sprouting from her husband's side.

Immortal and hermaphrodite they could not know of Good and Evil; know of anything save simple cell division. No potential. Winding down the World Tree's boughs, the Serpent of the double helix plots cold-blooded strategy.

If there is to be progress, then there must be sex.

There must be death, and all Earth's children, all the myriad creatures must destroy each other to survive.

Into mortality and evolution we descend.

We fall.

These dance-steps, Love and Death and Loss and War, are in our choreography from the beginning.

Here is Cromwell, wrapped in musket smoke.

Here is Rossetti, weeping by the grave side.

Here is Machen, watching Amy die and plunged into an abyss of grief.

Look closely at the dance, you'll notice that the woman leads.

The serpent lets her guide its every move.
Who is she?

See her circle.

See her tilt and arch and curtsey.

See her dip.

She is our solace and our comfort in this wilderness of stars.

When the bereaved Rossetti tries to resurrect his love in paint and canvas, it is she, sat at his side, who steers the brush; she who leads Machen out of pain and up the Hill of Dreams.

Look closer still and she is hardly there at all, pale and ethereal, translucent, made from moonlight. She is life's sole partner in this Waltz of Being, yet she is imaginary. More than this, she is Imagination, the most beautiful and splendid partner we could ever need; could ever hope for.

Naked save for moonshine, save the borrowed finery of Isis and Selene, she inspires our dance to new and unfamiliar steps, gives us the come-on. Sexier then anything, Imagination moves our feet upon the rungs of the genetic ladder, leads us from insensate slime and into consciousness. Dances us up from dumb, cold mud into the blazing heavens.

This, then, is the Universe, the great Romance: flesh and imagination cling and glide beneath a wash of stars.

Awareness spirals up, out from the weight and dark of conscious circumstance into the lunar shimmer up above.

Into the Dream.

The full text of this piece can be found in *A Disease of Language* (Knockabout 2005).

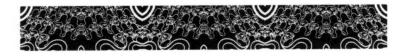

A. O. Spare, Self Portrait 1909,
from Borough Satyr: The Life and Art of Austin Osman Spare,
Fulgur, 2005. Reproduced with kind permission.

Imagination
Is What We Are
Erik Davis

*Edited from a talk given at
the Ojai Foundation, June 2008*

he visionary is what we are. The way we perceive the world is in a continuum with visionary experience and what the visionary means. So what we mean by 'visionary'? Of course, language itself is a visionary medium. Think of the images that come with reading poetry or a fine piece of prose or the sense of enchantment that a spell or a great ritual or a great invocation can produce.

We have visionary art, visionary poetry, visionary plants, visionary experience, and then we also have the sense of the visionary that you find in popular discourse. If you come across the word 'visionary' in *Time* Magazine, it's usually not talking about an ayahuascero or William Blake, usually it's talking about an entrepreneur. But it's actually a very interesting usage of the term, one that tells us something about one aspect of the visionary, which has to do with novelty and with being able to synthesise something new out of the bits and pieces of possibilities and realities.

Another sense of visionary is just having visions; seeing things that aren't quite there, or at least aren't there the way that ordinary objects seem to assert themselves. Dreams are, of course, the most obvious example of a kind of visionary experience, but I want to think a little bit more about the kinds of visions that we might perceive under ordinary circumstances in our daily lives.

The most obvious example that we all know, at least from being kids and then if we're lucky and chilled out enough to experience as adults, is the phenomenon of seeing faces in clouds or rock formations. Certainly true for me and I think it's true for a lot of people that you used to be able to do that more when you were a kid. As a kid you could look up at the clouds and you'd see a whole story unfold.

One of the greatest secondary gifts of meditation that I've ever had was during a Zen session. It was break time and I went out to do some stretching. It was a beautiful day and there were an unusual number of cumulus clouds hurtling through the sky over the Bay Area, which we don't usually get. I was looking at these and then something in my mind switched and I was five years old and watched an entire cartoon of coyotes and western landscapes and Indians and dragons all morphing and shifting.

We have a completely understandable tendency to see the patterns of faces in things. When you're a kid something that looks like a face is more likely to be Mom and more likely to give you some food. But that's not to reduce the phenomenon, because it's not just a face, it's a character: it's an old man, it's a wise woman, it's a kind of impish elf – whatever it is, there's an added imaginative force in this very simple experience of seeing faces in clouds. That ability to see a pattern or a form out of what is technically noise, or a random bunch of scratches, or marks on a tree, has to do with our ability to see patterns and that's one of the really remarkable thing about human consciousness. We can experience both literal, morphological patterns, but also a deeper sense of how things interrelate, how things interconnect, how things are brought together.

It seems that people vary quite dramatically in their ability to recognise patterns, and some studies show that there's a positive correlation between peoples' tendency to believe in religious or supernatural ideas and their tendency to perceive pattern.

On the one hand, you have people who have a resistance to fantasy, a resistance to a face appearing on a cloud because, after all, it's simply a cloud composed of random elements. And then on the other side, you have people who just see this stuff everywhere. And we've all known people like that: maybe it's that they've tapped into higher forces, or maybe it's just the way that their nervous system is organised. The idea that there's some correlation between that and supernatural or religious thinking makes a lot of sense. It's certainly true if you think about the way we perceive interconnection or synchronicity, because part of seeing pattern isn't just literally being able to see a visual pattern, it's also being able to pick out a pattern of events and have it seem like it has some meaning. You know: 'maybe it's not accidental that I saw that duck just as I was thinking about my father who I went duck hunting with and then I turned on the radio and they were playing cartoon music – it's all happening, it's something about ducks...'

And once again we've all had experiences of dipping into synchronicities, dipping into these deep patterns that seem to imply another level of meaning that's going on in the world. I want to suggest that this is part of the visionary function, that it's part of the visionary faculty, of being able to see those deeper patterns. So the idea that this goes along with a kind of supernatural or religious thinking seems very interesting to me because in addition to being able to make some linkages that are rich, it also gives us a little hint about how we practice with this stuff. How do we practice with the visionary? How do we cultivate that faculty? Why would we cultivate it?

This kind of visionary practice is also, as I mentioned before, a sort of metaphor for innovation. And that's the kind of popular sense we'll see of it now, where someone comes up with a new way of doing things, a new way of organising or structuring a business or exploiting the peculiarities of an information system – there's the sense of a deeper pattern emerging out of a set of possibilities.
What I think is important here is the idea of novelty, of something new, and something new that's not just a specific object but a new way, a crystallised pattern of doing things. The visionary isn't just 'oh I want to create a widget', it's usually a much larger scale pattern, like we think of Walt Disney as a visionary because he wasn't just saying 'oh we could make a park that has stuffed animals in it walking around talking to kids.' It's 'we're gonna create a new kind of world that's also a new kind of industry'. Even Ray Kroc of McDonalds can be seen in this light, because he saw a new way of changing urban space in a way that's not very pleasant but it is kind of visionary. He figured something out and it worked out really, really well. So what we can draw from this is that it's not just novelty but it's a way of drawing things together, it's profoundly synthetic, it's drawing links.

Another way of thinking about such practice is the relationship between the visionary and religion or spirituality. I'm particularly interested in the way in which the visionary as an idea, as a category, as a way of approaching reality and experience, allows us to see religion and religious experience in a new way. This acknowledges what is so profound and so attractive about spirituality and religion while avoiding some of the problems that people get into, usually around the question of belief.

The problem that a lot of people stumble on, especially secular people or scientific materialists but also just in general, is this idea that you have to *believe*, that the vision of what's important about Christ's resurrection is that it actually happened and you're either on the bus or you're off the bus. Then on the other side you have people who don't even want to pay attention to anything religious. They don't want to know about the deep metaphors in Genesis, they don't want to know about the visionary interpretations of the Book of Revelation. It's all just junk to them because they don't buy the essential belief structure. They don't believe in a God, so they don't need to pay attention to any of it. That's part of the sensibility that we see now with contemporary atheism. I think that appreciating the visionary as a category of perception and experience is a way to bring those worlds together. So instead of looking at the Bible as a collection of ossified belief systems, or as a claim about the nature of reality, we can see it as both a record of visionary experience and a kind of visionary poetry in itself.

Visionary poetry and aesthetic that has its own rules, its own sensibility. It's there in mythologies, in book-oriented systems like the Bible or the Quran and in more recent systems, the new mystery traditions and new forms of meditation and new systems of the occult. I think that one of the reasons that a lot of people are so attracted to different myth systems and different icons and different sacred sites is because they feed and magnify our own visionary sensibility. Even if we don't exactly *believe* in this material – hey, it's okay. All of this stuff can be seen as different ways of working with visionary experience – how you actually get into a state where the world appears differently, where perception changes and something new happens, something different happens – and then how you take that visionary experience into visionary expression, which might take the form of poetry, of art, of iconology, of architecture, of images, of rituals – any number of things.

33

If you adopt that perspective, of paying attention to visionary experience and the kind of poetic expression of these experiences that manifest in these different media, then suddenly a whole new way of looking at religion and spirituality opens up. I am reminded of when I went to Burma and went to the Shwedagon Paya in Yangon, one of my favorite sacred sites. This temple complex is on the top of a hill and there's temples all around in kind of a circle that surrounds an enormous central pagoda, and it's just full of these little cupulas. It's like a little city of the spirit, and walking through it is like walking through a visionary landscape. It's just that this visionary landscape has been built with material, with objects, it's fixed in meat-space, but it arose out of experiences and intuitions and poems and dreams over hundreds and hundreds of years.

And so I don't have to believe or not believe. The category of the visionary allows me to resonate with objects and images in a way that avoids that question. As such, I think it also lets us see a little bit more what are we doing when we turn to religion or, if we don't turn to religion, when we turn to ritual, when we turn to ceremony, when we turn to even the simple question of what do we wear to a spiritual event, what to do in the moments before and after meditation. These very simple aspects of ritual can be seen as ways of invoking this visionary space or this sense of visionary experience, which we can also think of as the imagination.

For the Romantics in the 19th Century, the imagination was an enormously important term. It was a central pavilion of the landscape, the city of the spirit. Often the way we use the word now is in the sense of 'oh that's just your imagination' – meaning you weren't really perceiving reality. Then there's the deeper sense of where ideas come from, where stories come from, where a good Hollywood set comes from. Then it's 'that person has a lot of imagination, they're able to come up with these things'. So that gives us a little stronger sense of it, but it's still mostly just limited to artistic creativity.

But there's a much bigger way of looking at the imagination. One of the persons that I like to turn to here is Coleridge, who is famous for his poem *Kubla Kahn,* which is subtitled *A Vision in a Dream; a Fragment.* The poem is not just visionary in the sense of its aesthetic power, it also has a great story attached to it of visionary experience. The well-known tale claims that the first portion of the poem was a direct channeling of a vision that was then rudely interrupted by the 'Person from Porlock', possibly his doctor. It's the most mundane thing. Coleridge loses the vision but writes the rest of the poem anyway. But when you read it you can tell where it happens, it's like something goes away and he begins to reflect on the vision and you go 'oh something broke there'.

What I love about that story is that it acknowledges how visionary experience continues to flow through the modern Western world, a world where we no longer have religious prophets. Instead we have artists and poets and some of them, we allow, have access to this kind of visionary experience. But the doctor breaking the spell is also an expression of our modern world, a sign of the quotidian realities that are blocking us. We have this longing for the visionary and yet it's difficult for us to get to. We often perceive the world as a very mundane place, and it almost constantly interrupts our attempts to generate that deeper sense of enchantment.

The hunger for the visionary is one of the things that draws modern people to spirituality and to religion and to poetry and to ritual and to celebration and to crazy parties and to eroticism. That attraction can also be mistaken. I think that we can mistake the visionary for aspects of reality that are perhaps more profound or should have a greater claim. Some of the delusion, for example, that arises around a lot of religious or spiritual seeking – either a fixedness on beliefs or a sort of mini-madness that encourages people to see patterns everywhere – arises because they're not really recognising the specific qualities of the imagination and the visionary that need to be cultivated. So we have issues around this hunger or desire for the visionary and it drives us in many ways. I mean the whole industry of Hollywood and videogames can be seen partly as a way to satisfy this desire for visionary experience in a way that perhaps could be done more artfully in a lot of cases. So to my mind we could try to become more aware of what this imagination can be, and how to cultivate and practice with it.

Coleridge was also a philosopher or a theorist, and he put forward the idea that there are two kinds of imagination – the primary and the secondary imagination. And the idea of the primary imagination he got largely from Immanuel Kant. Kant was facing an interesting problem. However it is that we know things, we know them from our own human perspective, with our own human ways of perceiving time and space and dimension. And it's really hard to get out of those categories. Kant thought that anything you perceived or anything you claimed about the nature of reality was always going to be in the context of these fundamental components of human consciousness. But he also faced the problem of how all those components come together and become experience. I'm here, I'm having a flow, all of these elements are somehow combining on the fly.

For Kant and for Coleridge, this act of synthesis is the responsibility of the primary imagination. The imagination in this view composes our sense of reality. It composes our sense of the various elements of experience – sensation, thought, memory, time, etc. – all being brought together in our apparently seamless flow. Coleridge also proposed a secondary form of imagination and this is the imagination more as we conventionally think about it, our artistic imagination. He wrote 'the imagination diffuses, dissolves and dissipates in order to recreate'. On the one hand this imagination samples elements, possibilities, partial ideas, and then it reforges them, it brings them together, it synthesises them. In some ways, it's a lot like the way dreams work. In reflection can see where a lot of the fragmentary elements were extracted from, but then it's recreated into something novel and occasionally extraordinarily beautiful and even meaningful.

So there's a deep continuity between our creative activities – whether this is in ritual or poetry or other forms of imaginative creativity – and our deeper and more fundamental sense of reality itself, of our own experience, of our own minds. Coleridge associated the primary imagination with the fundamental 'I am', that basic sense of self that sustains itself through reality. And this is why I said at the beginning that on some level I think the visionary is what we are, that right now we are having a visionary experience. It's constrained in certain ways, and because of our habituation we see it in certain ways, but in working more consciously with the imagination, with the visionary, we start to move into that subtle place where ordinary reality and extraordinary reality meet. And it's not that difficult. It can be scary, but it's not that difficult to take a healthy dose of a plant teacher and have visions. But what is perhaps more interesting is when we get to the crux of how the elements of the visionary are always right on the edge of our perception, right now. I think a lot of what ritual is, what an awake and creative attention to ordinary life can be, is a way of cultivating this kind of visionary sensibility.

So with that in mind, I want to turn to the idea of practice. Practice is a rejoinder to the idea of belief. If you do yoga and you talk about the chakras and you bring that up to a hard-headed scientist, they'll say 'what are you talking about, there's nothing there, it's irrational.' They're not even going to go there. And you reply 'But it's actually an interesting way to experience myself and my reality.' And how did you get there? By believing? By reading in a book and saying, 'oh, that's the system for me, there's seven chakras, I don't care about the five chakras the Tibetans use, there's seven chakras, and they work like this.' No, that's not how people do it. You're practicing yoga or you're reading a book that says 'check it out, do these meditations.' Then over time, as you willingly allow your imagination and its imprinting to interact with your body and with your practice, phenomena will occur – interesting phenomena, rich phenomena, phenomena that resonate with other things that you've been thinking or other things that you've been reading. Suddenly you go, 'I know exactly where my fifth chakra is, and I know exactly when it's open and when it's not.' And I'm sitting here talking to this scientist guy who says 'but there's no basis for that belief'. But that doesn't matter to me, I'm not on his map. I'm not belief or not-belief. I am practice. I practice with imagination and I practice with my body and certain experiences happen and I find it rich to continue to practice that way. I need no more justification.

The idea and the experience of practice are for me powerful ways of eluding some of the traps of spiritual belief and supernatural credulity. And they are also very ordinary ways, which is important. A lot of the issues that we face arise because we live in an ordinary reality a lot of the time, amid the texture of the mundane. We can have extraordinary experiences, we can go on fabulous trips, we can throw amazing parties, we can have great visionary experiences, but we have the sense of being thrown back into ordinariness. Practice is something that builds a bridge between these states, because there's something very ordinary about practice. There's something very sort of at-hand to it. I always feel like a kid practicing piano whenever I practice. The resonance of those words, those two kinds of 'practice,' is really, really important.

So what is visionary practice? What is imaginative practice? Once again I'll talk about the chakras, because it's something that everyone is more or less familiar with. Most of us have done meditation or yoga, and some of us have felt something like a chakra, or a concentration of energy. So how does it happen? How does it come about that I come to perceive something like my 'fourth chakra'?

One of the ways that it happens is that by changing your body you are producing a space or a potential for novelty. In our normal adult state, our being is hardened with certain kinds of habits that we hold in our bodies. And as you stretch and change and open up, you're physically creating the possibility of something new happening. You can understand that possibility in materialist terms: the way your skeletal structure distributes weight, or about how much tension you hold in your muscles, etc. But somewhere along the way, most of us ask the imagination to help do some of the work. So we meditate on a white light penetrating our skulls, or a green or golden wheel opening in our chests, a virtual object that is accompanied by a mantra. I may not believe in the chakras at all, but that chant sounds good, it hums, I can feel it resonating in my chest. So what I've done is use a practice to open up to a different level of experience, a sort of imaginative sensibility that finds itself once again in the world in which I see faces in clouds. And from that perspective I say 'okay, faces-in-clouds world, let's cultivate a golden sun that opens up in the center of my chest.' As I'm doing these physiological things, a deeper synthesis occurs, one that amplifies the body with the creative capacities of the imagination.

I think that a lot of the more profound visionary experiences that are accessible from such more or less ordinary states also have a strong *collective* dimension. If I go off on my own and just say there is an eighth chakra that's on my knee and it's purple and it looks like an octopus, yeah maybe that'll work. But probably not. Because part of what we're tapping into – and here we get a little bit woowoo – is, I believe, a collective and almost archeological dimension of the imagination.

> The imagination is never just inside your own skull. On a deeper level, on a more subtle level, the world of the imagination, the world of dreams, has a collective dimension. It is rich and thick and dense with the accumulated history of human experience: architecture and images in books and paintings on the wall and sounds and words and poems. After all, the imagination is partly

composed out of all of our human experiences. So when I'm turning to a traditional system like the chakras – although these too have evolved over time – it's not because they're right and the other guys are wrong. It's because there's so much richness there, there's so much density there, that I can tap into that and it can enter in and allow that collective field to begin to transform my individual experience.

A lot of traditional magic works that way. Let's say you're calling the quarters or you're practicing the lesser banishing ritual of the pentagram. As you're doing all this practice, with its physical and ritual elements, you are of course also involving the imagination. In that sense, ritual magic is very similar to yoga, where you're moving your body in a way that creates a space for something novel, a new program, a new kind of way of being in the body. But you're drawing the imagination into it and that's charging the operation much more.

The same thing when you simply call the elemental quarters. I remember when I first started to attend Neopagan rites. They would call the four directions, and I would wonder 'what are we doing, why are we calling these things?' I was so heady about it, like 'what, the spirits of the air, what does that mean?' And then I realized that what was being called was just a very different energy that came more from the heart and that it was almost like will or desire, like when I really wanted something. Eventually, it wasn't like wanting something that continues to me. Instead, it was *there* and it totally transformed my experience. So we tap into the energies of the body and the energies of the psyche in order to charge these practices and rituals of the imagination.

But what about this elusive word, energy? The most obvious energy is Eros, desire. If you take a form of the imagination, an image in a ritual context, and you bring desire or will to that energy, then suddenly you're really getting something going. That's part of what's going on with the emergence of the yogic chakra, it's part of what's going on with even the simplest ritual, like when I light a little stick of incense and set it before the Buddha before I sit on my cushion in the morning. There's a little bit of desire in there, there's a little bit of will, and this energy charges the imagination. Within ritual, desire transforms imagination into visionary practice. So part of the way we practice with the visionary, part of the way we practice with the imagination, is to become aware of those energies that we're bringing in.

For one thing the body is always involved in some way or another, along with the energies of the psyche. And of all these energies, it is desire, or Eros in the classical sense, that is really the key element. If you go back and look at the history of magic, you find some amazing descriptions of the models of the body and soul that explained how magic actually works. In particular, there's a whole tradition, going back to Aristotle, of trying to understand where the images in your head come from. Where do these phantasms come from? What's the relationship between the objects that I see in the world and the objects I can imagine with my eyes closed or that I see in my dreams? What's actually making that happen? Over the centurires people created elaborate systems to explain this. One was the concept of *pneuma* -- a material that was inside you, that was associated with the breath, and that would get impressed with images. Phantasms were therefore considered to be actually internal image-things that would work inside of us. There were different practices to charge these phantasms, and to use them to control or inspire others.

The motive force that was connecting these images, that connected the phantasm in my head to the objects that I saw in the world, to the spirits of the heavens or the planetary bodies which were all connected in a kind of astrological way – that energy was Eros, desire. Eros, in this classical and Renaissance idea, functions much like the way I earlier described visionary innovation as synthetic or dreams as synthetic. There's this activity of drawing together and fusing and making anew that's fundamental to the visionary and it has a great deal to do with desire, the desire to bring together, to connect, to bond, to fuse, to become one.

In most people's experience, the closest they come to genuine enchantment is falling in love. What's going on there, according to this theory of phantasms? The image of the other has entered in and become a phantasm in my mind, where it is charged with this tremendous longing and desire that resonates on all these different levels. So I'm having a theophany when I see the loved one, the same way that Moses has a theophany of God in the burning bush. And that, itself, is a portal into my mind, into the way that the visionary works. There's a certain quality of desire, a certain quality of attraction, and a certain relationship to the image that's very powerful, and spiritual.

Love, in this sense, is a sacred practice, and desire a cultivation of the visionary.

The last thing I want to talk about here is the extraordinary visionary practices associated with plant allies and medicines. This is a different zone of the imagination, because there's just so much there and it can be so overwhelming, and so tricky. Most of the time, we're on the mundane plane and little glimpses of the visionary waft through. In these extraordinary states it's the opposite: we're overwhelmed with the extraordinary and sometimes find ourselves craving a little bit of mundane! And so it becomes a different kind of question of how to practice with these images.

First let's look at the liminal space, the in-between zone, that we go through to get there. What actually happens as we go from here to there? One of the great gifts of these compounds is that when you are coming on and they're first opening up the visionary world, you can see how the visionary capacity itself emerges from your conventional perception. You can also see this while going to sleep sometimes. If you're lucky you can watch in a hypnogogic state how the dreamworld begins, but in a way that links it to entheogens. This has happened to me a number of times, and it has helped me understand one dimension of visionary pharmacology.

If I manage to stay conscious as I fall asleep, what do I see? Initially there is nothing but neurological fireworks going off on the dark screen of my closed eyelids. I can see phosphene activity, random squiggles of light, a little zigzag here and there, maybe a circle, but not much going on. Then suddenly, some of these random bits form a pattern, a triangle, let's say. And then – this is the interesting part – the triangle turns 3D and it becomes a pyramid and I'm on the deserts of Arabia, with a caravan moving along like the beginnings of a story. Pretty cool. I moved from neural randomness, from mere noise, to a basic kind of pattern recognition, and then that pattern bloomed into an image and then a realm, into a dynamic interactive realm. If I continue to go deep I'm gonna meet other characters in there and they're gonna tell me stuff and they're gonna take me to other realms and it keeps going on and on and on.

One important aspect of the teaching of visionary plants, at least in my view, is that these visions themselves are not necessarily that important. It's not that you must take them on, that they're your spiritual work, the 'message' you need to understand. That's not necessarily what the plants are telling you, or teaching. Part of what they're teaching is just how it is that visions come to be, how it is that your mixture of memory and the mysterious archetypal immensity of the deep imaginal realms come to impinge on this nervous system, in this situation, at this moment.

41

Part of visionary practice, in otherwords, is disenchanting the visions. Not making them meaningless, not saying they're just random noise, but rather understanding how they're constructed. Because the more you understand how they're constructed, how the visionary comes to be, the more you can cultivate that sensibility in a very ordinary, but very constructive, way in your mundane life. When we cease to believe that the visions come from without, and that instead they emerge from the vast potential within, then we can begin to build avenues for their emergence throughout all the realms, from the most sublime to the most quotidian. Art, ritual, techniques of perception, meditation, love making, gardening, research – all these become a facet of visionary practice.

Dreams of a
Midwich Planet
Stephen Grasso

 bright, accusing sun rises high over a city scattered with small, budding secrets and mysteries. The dull glow of magic easing up out of the ground, quiet and unnoticed, between concrete tower blocks and red brick houses. Threadbare sorcerers and motheaten magicians growing sullenly between the paving stones. Tiny pioneers hiding away in anonymous lodging houses and meagre bedsitting rooms. A consortium of small men and dispossessed ladies masturbating tiredly over paper symbols to nudge a promotion at work or a small win on the lottery. Voicing lacklustre admonitions to half-remembered powers, shy petitions to gain entry into the hallowed mysteries of the office receptionist's pants. Row upon row of hungry conjurors feverishly employing dusty, antique spells to speed the delivery of their hastily scribbled wishes. Is this the shape of our magic? Is this all we can imagine for ourselves? Are these the limits of our expectation?

Black Jacky Johnson, who outwitted the devil and walked with a perpetual limp from the night he spent in hell back in 1862. The terrible shopkeeper of 'Blackened Fortunes' that once stood on Grainger Street in Newcastle and sold cures and curses to those brave enough to ask for them. The cruel ex-blacksmith who could speak with dogs and horses, who carried a stick that had its own heartbeat, and who gave a wink and walked out of the world one cold spring morning.

Papa Dynamite, who fought the law and won. Who could heal the sick with his penis and was afraid of no man. Who held court in the upstairs room of 'The Ocean' on Portobello Road. Always in full evening dress, sometimes with a boa constrictor draped over his shoulders. Who listened to the problems of the people who came to him and helped where he could. Who put the fear into threepenny gangsters, slum landlords and peers of the realm. Who discovered a secret in June

1966 that made him so angry that his fury almost shattered the British Government of the day.

Gypsy Agatha, who could read the future in an old bowler hat filled with strange liquids, her unlikely prophecies all coming true within seven days. Who made amulets out of bone and feathers that could snare any man, potions and perfumes that could lure any woman. Her body tattooed with a secret map of the doorways, power spots and soft places of Lancashire. Who gave wicked council in matters of the heart to fish wives and wealthy ladies, and continued to savagely deflower the countless heartbroken girls and boys who flocked to her caravan for help, long into her sixties, in return for granting their heart's desire. Who drank neat gin and bragged to sailors that she harvested the lost virginity of her customers in a copper lined jar, but to what end and for what purpose?

Tony Cunningham, who lived in a crooked house filled with umbrellas. Who was terrified of the night sky on a midsummer's eve, tended a garden of curious plants, and consorted with pale hopping creatures on the moors at night. Who packed a suitcase one morning and travelled the length and breadth of England on a tandem bicycle, with his invisible benefactor Yellow Morgan in tow, dispensing his sorceries to those in need. Who saved the lives of eighteen miners trapped beneath the earth by striking a hard bargain with oak, ash and elm that he regretted till the end of his days.

43

Mammy Winter, who smoked cigars and walked barefoot in all seasons. Who claimed she had stopped something terrible from happening to Scotland in 1663 but could never tell a soul or it would be undone. Who could see through the eyes of jackdaws and magpies, understood the language of cats, and kept the people of her village safe from harm when the black plague was raging through Europe. Who lost her beauty in a game of cards, froze up her heart and baked her only daughter into a pie.

I conjure up these spirits to look upon us and despair. Here are your children. Austere characters in off-the-peg robes intoning barbarous names out of a textbook and imitating the gestures of a bald British heroin addict long dead. Career occultists jostling for a publishing deal, the holy grail of popular magic, empowered by the gods of mediocrity to churn out book after book of the same old, same old. Armchair theorists spitting out rules and boundaries on enchantments they have never touched, secrets they have not earned, Spirits that are unknown to them.

Generations of witchdoctors with their hands tied and their mouths bound, dreaming of gaunt apparitions, clockwork ghosts and a feast of crows. Their passions reduced to empty theory and formula. Assailed by post-modern posturing and glib experiment passed off as innovation. Sparks of brilliance few and far between, discouraged and drowned beneath an endless regurgitation of tired ideas, book learning, and untested assumptions. The carcass of the mysteries picked bare by scavenging pop psychologists and pseudo-scientists.

It ends tonight. We grew up believing in magic. We made an uneasy alliance with the witch who lived beneath the stairs and befriended the tiny men that lived at the top of the curtains and could come into our dreams. We held lengthy conversations with our own shadows about the myriad flickering worlds only they are privy to. Consulted bird tables that revealed the future to us in sparrow droppings, feathers and walnut shells. Collected seaweed, stones and pebbles from the beach and made elaborate patterns with them on the sand, secret messages for the ocean that nobody else understood. Planted wishes in the garden and watered them every day with milk and orange juice until they took shape. Kept a box of treasures and knew that each one opened a doorway to a far off land, if we could only figure out how they worked.

One day we were told that none of it was real. We were pressured to give up the validity of these dreams and put away childish things. They brought us a brass key with the slippery and seductive word 'grown-up' marked on it, and hinted at the new mysteries it could unlock. We turned the key and nervously shuffled through. Joined furtive circles made of cigarette smoke that curled defiantly in hidden corners of the schoolyard, drank forbidden sacraments of cheap white cider beneath lonely monuments and in the shadow of abandoned bus shelters, and learned of strange insertions that brought inestimable delight.

We looked upon these things and saw that they were good, but still we remembered a world where orange crayons could be used to speak with spiders, and the gaps between cobbled paving stones were home to an entire kingdom of tiny insect warriors. We looked for magic in a world that shunned and mocked such things. Hunted for glimpses of it in neglected places, on an overlooked alcove of the library, in a tattered cardboard box at the second-hand shop, left behind with the dregs of the car boot sale that nobody else wanted.

One day we found some magic and took it home. It wasn't what we remembered. It gave us hard plastic holes in which to fit the curious misshapen dreams that we kept in our heart. Still, we learned our lesser banishings and greater hexagrams, how to invoke and evoke, and deal in servitors, egregores and archetypes. We learned about a great many things and some of us even did them. Yet in our irresolute and unguarded moments we felt the nagging suspicion that something was missing.

It kept us awake at night. We couldn't see the shape of the uncertain beast that haunted us. We tried to explain our disquiet to others but got only blank stares in response. Gradually the source of our apprehensions crept more clearly into view. Magic was far bigger, wilder and stranger than we had been led to believe. Our sorceries are like a wild hawthorn tree that has been forced to grow inside a warehouse packed to the brim with boxes of assumption and crates of empty bluster. Twigs and creeping branches have wound themselves tightly around stale ideas and second-hand theory, when it is their nature to stretch out proudly into fierce, undiscovered territory. Leaves of hope and enthusiasm have reddened too soon and fallen on a stark, concrete floor, when it is their nature to blossom into bright, phantasmagoric colour and give off dangerous fruit. The bark of our magic has grown dry, cracked and hollow, when it should be strong, vigorous and teeming with life.

Meagre pickings for a world eating its own tail. A pitiful breakfast of spells served up to a frightened planet. It can't continue on like this. Something has to change. This world has no need for legions of self-satisfied men mouthing pompous words to their imaginary friends or ranks of complacent women reciting nursery rhymes over a campfire. It needs its magicians to come out of hiding and step up to the challenge of setting their affairs in order. The time has come for us to stop practising our magic and start putting it to work.

45

We treat our sorcery as if it were a parlour game or weekend hobby, forgetting that it is a profession and a role. There is a reason and a purpose for these things beyond our own amusement. The planet cries out for its magicians to remember their function. The earth groans beneath the burden of a task unfulfilled. Something is not being done. We can't sit on our hands any longer. We're the children of magicians. Our ancestors bequeathed us words of power, ways and means, subtle devices, hidden knowledge, skills and wisdom. They were not handed down to us for empty recitation or performance art. There is a job that needs to be done.

It's the role of magicians to get their hands dirty in the places that other people are afraid to go, to speak to the universe and try to understand its nature, to traffic with invisible intelligences on behalf of the wider community, and seek to create meaning for the species we belong to. We have to learn how to use every trick in the book, master all the secrets that our ancestors knew, and strive to refine and improve on this body of knowledge. We must become the most potent and effective generation of magicians that this world has ever seen, because when the future comes, it takes no prisoners. Those are the stakes.

It's all down to us now, nobody else is going to do this thing. No ancient masters or secret chiefs are going to come in and clean up the mess. There's just us, and we have to get it done. It's our turn to pick up the torch and run with it. To the finish line if we have to.

It's happening now.

Sally Lords has lived by the sea all her life. When she was a little girl her grandmother used to take her for long walks along the promenade. She would eat candy floss and ice cream, chase seagulls down the road, spend her pocket money in the amusement arcade and then run down to the sands for a story. Her grandmother would fill her head with tales of her own mother and a host of distant aunts and relatives, and the adventures they used to have in the village.

There was Jemima Lords, the Northumbrian sea witch, who brought Charlie Golightly home from a watery grave after he'd been missing at sea for seven nights. Who made old pacts and alliances with mermaids, undines and spirits of the deep. There was Sofia Lords, who could show unmarried girls the face of their future husband in the dank waters of rock pools in return for a penny. Sarah Lords, the midwife, who never lost a child. Howard Lords, who married a mermaid princess and disappeared beneath the waters. Lisa Lords, whose good manners and bargaining provided safe passage and full shoals for the village's fishermen during the bitter winter of 1784.

Sally treasured her grandmother's stories and would sometimes pretend to be brave Jemima or wicked Anna Lords, who had cursed the village for seven years. She would have tea parties with sand and seaweed, hold made-up conversations with starfish and hermit crabs, and constantly worry her parents by always swimming much too far out into the water by herself. The tall tales of her ancestors thrilled her heart, and she knew that when she grew up she wanted to be just like them.

At school she was bright, but prone to day dreaming and flights of fancy. Her teachers complained that she would frequently stare out of the window during lessons, and then be furious when chastised for it, as if the billowing waves were more worthy of her time and attention than the classroom. She left at sixteen and went to work on the checkouts at the local supermarket, slept with a boy, and gave birth to a baby called Rosie.

On new year's eve, just after her twenty-first birthday, she first started having the dreams. It was the same thing every night. A terrifying, hallucinogenic vision of the raging sea. Her tiny body awash and at the mercy of vast, unnatural waves. A deafening rush of water pounding her skull. Her senses addled by endless, violent waters. Her heart chilled with the primal fear of something terrible moving quickly beneath her in the deep.

When Sally's grandmother died in the spring, her uncertainty was suddenly gone. She woke up early one morning, put on the silver locket that had been left to her, and went down to the shore. She lit a white candle before the sea, and prayed to her ancestors – all of the great ladies and subtle gentlemen of her bedtime stories – and she asked them what it was that she must do.

They had been waiting for her all along, and slowly she began to learn. She listened to the sea and it furnished her with songs. She went for long walks along the beach at dawn and received many treasures washed up on the lonely sand. Signs and portents, a message in a bottle, driftwood sticks and seashell oracles, all the tools of her trade. She visited her ancestors with offerings every Sunday, spent long hours in conversation with the dead, and a nascent grasp of her role began to blossom intuitively within her.

47

She asked for introductions and they were granted. She rekindled all the old alliances with the Mother of Fishes, the Beautiful Siren, the Captain of the Seven Seas, and the Prince of Pirates. She learned how to call undine daughters from the waters and charm them to perform spirit work. She learned how to sing songs that could calm the storm or stir the seas into motion. Steadily, a rich knowledge and understanding of the Mysteries rose like sunken debris from the dark ocean bed of her being into the light of consciousness.

Sally turned her space on the supermarket tills into an elaborate shrine to the ocean spirits, decorated with shells and seaweed, blue beads and photographs, cockles and mussels, starfish, sand paintings and the fruits of the deep. Nobody dared question her. She sat at the heart of her town and began to serve the mysteries by caring for the desperate people who passed her way. Lonely ladies would come to her with their groceries and furtively ask for their fortunes to be read in the shells. Battered wives would seek her counsel and protection. Despondent girls and pitiful boys would visit in tears and leave with something extra and enchanted surreptitiously slipped into their shopping bags. They came with their troubles and heartache, fears and failures, and Sally was always there.

Then the drums began to sound again on the beach at night. Sally waited and soon enough they came. The curious and the brave, the lost and the needful. They heard the drum patterns on the wind and something in their hearts responded, nervously compelling them to put aside worldly things for awhile and go down to the shore to celebrate their mother, the ocean. The infinite, rolling womb from which all life was born, and the source of the watery mysteries that flow within us.

In time, the numbers started to grow. More and more people from the village and surrounding areas appeared on the beach each month, and Sally would always be there to lead them in celebration of the ocean's mysteries. A raft filled with offerings would be pushed out to sea for the Mother of Fishes, the rhythms would start to pound, and the night would come alive with music and dancing beneath a fat moon and a sky filled with stars.

Sally's midnight ceremonies fulfilled a need in them that had long been neglected. The dances she held gave shopkeepers and bankers, plumbers and sex workers, builders and criminals a chance for open communion with the mysteries and a window into the numinous. No-one was turned away and nobody left without a taste of direct contact with the mysteries. Those who came to her ceremonies always returned.

48

Magic stretched out from Sally and reached into the lives of everyone around her. It gave hope, support and meaning where there had been emptiness, confusion and sorrow. It fixed unsolvable problems, took away fear and despondency, and put power back into the hands of the disempowered. It picked up the thread of evolution and tied it to the ankle of the species, a beautiful great ape shambling roughly into tomorrow.

It's happening now. In broad daylight, just around the corner, at the end of your road. Something new and fierce wipes the dirt from its brow, bites through its umbilical chord and walks abroad in the world for the first time.

Untitled - Nathaniel Ritter

Someone is Messing with the Big Picture, II
Carl Abrahamsonn

ooking through my notes for the talk at the Equinox Festival 2009, I find a lot of moping and complaining, some bitter and almost cynical remarks that would strike me as negative had I heard them from another's mouth. Be that as it may, but I thought this catalogue's companion text would be a good place to make slightly more sweet-tasting amends.

Equinox, as we know, is a time of cosmic balance and joyful celebration. Don't we all wish that it could be Equinox all year long? But it seems to be a fact that nothing is ever static or rigid – well, except for quite a few human minds – and for this we should be grateful. To go with the flow is better than to rest in the nest.

That we presently need change seems obvious to us all. I'd like to paraphrase the current American president's 'A change we can believe in' (Isn't that what most Americans like to do – believe?) and move it onwards to 'A change we can tangibly develop through'. Life is about a lot more than saving the economy. A wider equinoctial balance seems so far away and so important that we can't really leave it to the politicians anymore. After all, they are only human.

If I complain about speed, fragmentation, minimalisation, condescension, infantilisation etc, what remedies do I have? Well, their opposites of course. How hard can it be? Slowness, holistics, maximising and increasing the scale, appreciating maturity and wisdom... Very basic things.

I do believe we need to turn on, tune in and drop a lot of imposed rubbish. And I'm still naive enough to believe that art is how we should go about it. The hubris stemming from our very real anthropocentric insignificance is about to destroy... Well, at least our own habitat but possibly more than that too. The planet as such does not need to be saved, but an ecosystem suitable for human beings certainly does. How could art change that?

Well, necessity always makes itself heard, just like a bowel movement. We are becoming re-minded of nature. We need to merge with nature on every level, to be able to be a part of the totality of existence. As we need to merge with nature, art needs to merge with a mind that's capable of seeing this bigger picture. If that doesn't happen, we will all still be tiny dictators sucking poisoned nectar through ever thinning straws. Basic survival equals knowledge, information, science if you will, and feeding. But advanced development requires inspiration, communication and feedback. Where do we find this? In art.

The initiative for a festival like this is brilliant and well-needed in this respect. Crossovers, mind-mergers, non-static disciplines uniting if but for an hour or two, non-rigid traditions and colourful people meeting, talking, watching, listening and perhaps even learning from each other. This festival is a solvent in which agents charge and discharge. What more could one really ask for?

Special kudos to Ralph Metzner who has been synthesising these important concepts for such a long time. Blessings! When we chatted in Stockholm in 2004, Ralph formulated his basic view very well: 'My interest is the knowledge and understanding that can be gained from expanded states of consciousness. States of consciousness can be contracted and pathological as well. But the expanded ones are more interesting for me. How do you build them and turn them into a lasting condition? Say, if someone is depressed, they don't want to be undepressed for a little while. How can you hang on to a state of mind that's lasting and get to the bottom of your personal problems for instance. How do we integrate such states?'

Isn't that 'the call of the artist' right there? How to integrate whatever you have or have experienced and give it a more or less universal form that resonates with other people?

Sharing is not only about generic altruism. It's also about deliverance from and release of pressure on an individual level. We need to share the findings or formulations for our own sake too. We are social animals. We experience insights and stunning synchronicities. These enrich our lives but even more so if we can communicate them to others.

The sexual allegory is not far-fetched here (is it ever?). There are solitary means of seeking release for gathered emotions, fantasies, desires etc. But for most people it is actually more stimulating and satisfying seeking that release with someone else. Not forgetting the creative potential of that kind of meeting. There needs to be penetration and energies in circulation.

Tradition and mere habitual life essence is not enough. In this day and age, ceremonies are not needed as much as transforming rituals. Who really needs safe slogans or simplified techno-gaga? Simplification becomes more and more complex by the day. Terminology: a trap of

51

reason fragmenting potential unity. However, storytelling, parables, allegories, metaphors, symbols are all part of the language of survival. That language, I suspect, will be non-rational, non-intellectual, and non-language-based as we're used to it. If so, it might just work.

A potential communication from mind to mind, with or without filtering matrices, structures, agents, solvents or grids, will be the language of the future. Technology in itself will not be our saving grace. Lack of technology will, however. That freedom and the challenge in itself will in turn open up new vistas of inter-human, inter-planetary, inter-stellar and even inter-galactic communication. Messages from mind to mind, for and through new dimensions.

That said, I wonder why so much of contemporary art is still stuck in the usual commodified two or perhaps, if we're lucky, three dimensions? The territorial urination of and on the art market? Is there a distinct parable there to human life in general? I think so, unfortunately. Culture and art needs to pave the way, as always.

52

Two examples have recently provided me with a glimmer of hope. Both are Swedish artists, but that isn't really relevant on any other level than that they're from my own sphere, so to speak.

Fredrik Söderberg creates non-rational expressions by experimenting with geometry, mathematics, linearity. He is very much a mandalic artist, a skilled craftsman and draughtsman who merges with spiritual inclinations in a holistic unity. Traces of esoteric and religious history are filtered for the future through structures which challenge and stimulate the human senses and brains. Sheets of colourful emanations can become vivifying gates to new worlds. Those grids and levels of awareness are readily available.

Gustaf Broms is a ritualist, a magician, an eco-thinker who in every piece expresses will – and love. Regardless of whether he's on a year-long walk from Sweden to the Ukraine with his partner Trish Littler or if he's making earth sculptures in the Australian desert or scrubbing the city centre of Stockholm on his knees or meditating at rush hour peaks in the most condensed and stressed epicentre of commuterised Stockholm, et cetera et cetera, it's all made with a vision much, much larger than awakening interest in this or that gallery. Those grids and levels of awareness are readily available.

A hypothetical example for the British: if a highly successful artist like D* H* would like to be rememebered in art history for things other than engorged revenues and colourful commodities, he could perhaps invest all of his wealth in spraying the entire globe with hemp seed? I can see an armada of carriers and bombers spraying the planet with this remarkable, oxygen-providing weed. This kind of direct approach to art could be a healthy, relevant and decidedly intriguing development. One where art is no longer symbolic and programmatic but rather direct and beneficial on more levels than the intellectual. Again, those grids and levels of awareness are readily available.

Art feeds back. We make the art that feeds us, and we in turn feed art further. After the act of creation, art stands alone. Magic stands alone. Literature stands alone. Music stands alone. Human beings? Certainly not.

The artist used to be a high character who was revered and feared for being able to create change in accordance with will – his or her own, or that of the whole tribe. The analogy today would be the figure of the lobbyist, the PR-person advocating bribery, lying and loss of all ideals to pragmatically satisfy a 'client'. Yes, these are sad times and black magic is apparently more lucrative than ever before.

Celebrity worship is a tragic case of false idols taking charge. People are looking for answers to undefined emotional questions but find only evanescence and empty barrels creating loud echoes. Autographs used to be examples of talismanic transference but now, apparently, mass-produced items, records, CDs, DVDs are sufficient. Items charged with the soul of the magical creator? A very shallow, impoverished and transparent Zeitgeist (literally 'time-ghost') it seems.

53

It's obviously important to make decisions wherever and whenever you can. But in a cultural sphere in which we are, at least on the surface, encouraged to do so (although most of us know that's just a politically and commercially convenient illusion) it can also be a very relevant decision to remain outside the generic process (the 'loop' as it's been so aptly called) and sow seeds in a much more fertile soil.

Art stands out, in my mind at least, as the most fertile soil available to us today. Perhaps because it's a sphere, like the Earth itself, that becomes ever more fertile the more manure is heaped onto it by critics and enemies.

Impression. Will. Expression. Manifestation.

Four cyclically bound words that have changed life always as well as forever and a day. Good luck!

Stockholm, April's Fools Day, 2009

Shamanism, Yoga & Alchemy
Dr Ralph Metzner

rom the most ancient times, human beings have practiced disciplines of psychospiritual and physical healing. Of the three great traditions of consciousness transformation which have appeared on Earth, shamanism is the oldest, dating to Paleolithic times, and preserved in indigenous cultures worldwide to this day. Yoga and alchemy can be regarded as the Eastern and Western extensions or developments of shamanism respectively, originating in Neolithic village cultures and Bronze Age city states. In all three of these traditions, some aspects were more focussed on physical healing, some more on psychological problem solving and obtaining guidance for living, yet others on the quest for spiritual knowledge, enlightenment or liberation. Many of our modern systems of psychotherapy, of complementary healing and spiritual practice are the inheritors of one or another strand of these traditions.

Divination practices are found in all three of these traditions. In essence, divination involves a structured inquiry into questions of the past – for healing and resolving problems; or of the future – for visioning and obtaining guidance. In medicine, these two kinds of divination correspond to diagnosis, assessing the causal origin of an illness or injury, and prognosis, its probable future outcome.

Mircea Eliade, who wrote authoritative volumes on each of the three traditions of transformation, referred to shamanism as archaic techniques of ecstasy. The word 'ecstasy' derives from 'ex-stasis', being 'out of the state,' out of the perceptual framework of ordinary reality, or in an altered state of consciousness. In indigenous cultures, the metaphor for entering into an altered state of consciousness is the shamanic journey: like an ordinary journey, the shamanic state of consciousness has a beginning, a certain duration with various experiences, and an ending, the return to ordinary life (or ordinary consciousness). The shaman goes on a shamanic journey for a purpose, which might be healing, or diagnostic divination, or connecting with the spirits of deceased ancestors. He/she goes on the journey on behalf of an indivdual, or a family or a community that seek his or her help.

There are two main technologies for entering into the shamanic journey state, that are found worldwide: rhythmic drumming or rattling and psychoactive plants or fungi. Both these methods can induce changes in brain functioning, which form the neuro-physiological substrate for the divination journey. The drumming method appears widespread in the Northern hemisphere areas of Asia, Europe and North America. The psychoactive plants and fungi are more usually found in the tropical latitudes, particularly Central and South America, and Africa – presumably because of the much greater diversity of plant and animal life in the tropics.

55

In the earlier part of the 20th Century, psychologists and psychiatrists reading the anthropological accounts of shamans, tended to denigrate them as 'witch doctors' and purveyors of superstitious tribal beliefs. The practices of the shamanic divination journey were regarded as fraudulent or schizophrenic. Under the influence of the cultural relativism school of anthropology and the work of scholars such as Mircea Eliade, Margaret Mead, Ruth Benedict and Michael Harner, these views have given way to an undertanding that shamans and the cultures in which they exist live in a completely different worldview, with different assumptions about the nature of reality.

The two principal differences between the worldview of shamanistic indigenous cultures and the modern worldview of scientific materialism are: (1) the conception of multiple 'worlds' or multiple levels of reality and consciousness; and (2) the recognition of the reality of spirits as autonomous beings inhabiting the many worlds (rather than being mere fantasies or symbols). The worldview underlying shamanism, as well as alchemy and yoga, is known as animism or panpsychism – the belief that all the forms of nature, both the organic (e.g. plants, animals, fungi) and the inorganic (e.g. stones, rivers, mountains, winds), both the terrestrial (i.e. this planet Earth) and the cosmic (other planets, stars, galaxies, universe) are imbued with psychic or spiritual energy and consciousness.

Psychologically speaking, from within the Western scientific worldview, one could say that the concepts of 'other worlds' refer to levels or realms of consciousness that lie outside the boundaries of our usual and ordinary perception. The depth psychologies derived from psychoanalysis refer to such normally inaccessible realms as 'the unconscious', or 'the collective unconscious.' This would, however, be too limiting a definition for shamanism, if 'unconscious' is taken to refer to something within the human psyche. Shamanic practices involve the exploration not only of unknown aspects of our own psyche, but also the unknown aspects of the world around us – the external as well as internal mysteries. Similarly, psychologists would say that all references to 'spirits' are really symbolic expressions for aspects of the human unconscious psyche; and in the case of Jung's psychology, archetypal symbols of the collective unconscious. Western paradigms of reality are in need of being revised and expanded to include the recognition of the reality of spirits, as not just symbolic constructions of the human mind, but as living, intelligent, autonomous beings, with whom it is possible to communicate and with whom we co-exist and interact in the multiple worlds of reality.

Shamanic healing practices involve connecting consciously with the spirits of plants or fungi, whether nutritive, medicinal or visionary; and such a perspective is also found in homeopathy and traditional herbal medicine of many cultures. When travelling to other realms, shamans will invoke the Spirit of an animal species, such as Bear or Eagle, with which they have formed an alliance or collaborative relationship. Shamans may also work with crystals and other material earth substances, as well as with elemental spirits of air (wind), water (rivers, rain), and fire. Another important large class of spirits with whom shamans communicate and collaborate are the spirits of deceased ancestors. Then there are the greater ancestral, guiding and teaching spirits of whole tribes and peoples, traditionally known as 'gods' or 'deities', that play such a significant role in the world's many mythologies. Finally, the whole Earth itself is seen in traditional cultures as imbued with an intelligent, spiritual being, a goddess known as Gaia among the ancient Greece, or Mother Earth among North American Indian tribes. The modern scientific Gaia theory of James Lovelock and Lynn Margulis in many ways parallels and converges with ancient indigenous conceptions – seeing the Earth as an integrated living system, self-maintaining and self-organising. And not only the Earth but also the Sun, Moon and other planets are recognised in ancient and indigenous cultures as the bodies of cosmic deities – the planets still have the names the ancient Greeks and Romans gave to these deities.

Yoga, like shamanism and alchemy, comprises a certain kind of world view, as well as systematic technologies for expanding and raising consciousness. Mircea Eliade's classic work in this field – Yoga, Immortality and Freedom – points to the essential belief in the immortality of the soul or spirit, and to the pathways of liberation from the bondage of illusion and attachment. The word yoga derives from the Sanskrit root yuj – to link, connect or unite: the essential aim of all yoga practices is to connect with the essential spiritual core of the human being. In our ordinary states of consciousness the awareness of our spiritual essence is blocked by superimposed images and obstructions (klesas), principally a kind of unconsciousness (avidya or 'not-knowing'), and hence the yogic path is described as one of liberation from these blockages.

There are many strands within the yogic tradition. Some are focussed on the physical level (hatha yoga), some more on the emotional, devotional aspect (bhakti yoga), some on the mental, intellectual (jñana yoga). There are many variations in terminology in the texts that describe different aspects of the practices of yoga: raja yoga is the 'royal path' of psychological exercises; nada yoga and shabda yoga are the practices of working with sound and tone; tantra yoga, like raja and kundalini yoga refers to practices of visualisations of color and form symbols in the subtle energy field with its energy centers, or chakras.

Compared to the shamanic and alchemical traditions, there is less emphasis in the yogic traditions on connecting with nature, animals, plants, minerals or metals, and more focus on developing interior, higher, more refined states of consciousness and subtle perceptions. Of course, the ancient Indian medical system of Ayurveda does include the physical and breathing practices of yoga along with the use of herbal and mineral preparations in healing. In some strands of the Indian yoga teachings, particularly of the Samkhya school, there is an emphasis on rigorous detachment from and transcendence of the realms of nature, matter and the physical body. Important exceptions to this general tendency are tantra yoga in India and Tibet, and Taoist yoga practices in China, both of which are closely allied to alchemy in those cultures. Alchemy in India and China, as well as Tantra and Taoism, emphasize the transmutation of the physical body and practices of regeneration and longevity, along with the seeking of higher, transcendent states of consciousness.

Agni yoga is a term and practice from an older layer of tradition in India: Agni is the name of the ancient Vedic fire deity, whose name was invoked in elaborate rituals and prayers around an exterior fire altar. As a yogic path, it refers to practices of working with the interior light-fire energy centers and currents to purify the nadis, the field lines of the subtle electro-magnetic energy-field. References to inner light-fire are also found in the reports of shamanic practioners, as well as the mystical traditions of all religions, in which light and fire (or, as we would say today, 'energy') are recognised as the essence of all reality and all being. The principle of purification by (inner) fire is also one of the key operations of the alchemical tradition.

Alchemy, which developed independently in Europe, the Near East, India and China, shares with shamanism the goal of consciousness transformation, the quest for healing and knowledge, and the profound respect for Nature. The psychospiritual purposes and techniques of the alchemists came in time to be all but forgotten, and overshadowed by its applications in the experimental physical sciences.

Modern schools of psychotherapy, especially those based on psychodynamic depth psychology and the newer so-called 'experiential therapies', employ many of the methods and techniques of consciousness change that were known in the ancient systems of shamanism, alchemy and yoga. In some instances, for example in both Freud's and Jung's borrowing of alchemical ideas, the derivation is quite conscious and deliberate; in other cases, for example the use of inner journeys or imagery sequences, psychologists are rediscovering or reinventing methods that have been known and practiced for centuries in these older traditions.

58

In his book *The Forge and the Crucible*, Mircea Eliade posited that alchemy grew historically out of the work of shamanic miners, smiths and metallurgists, starting in the Bronze Age. They were the masters of fire, who knew how to extract metals from stone, blend them into alloys such as bronze, and how to make tools, weapons and ornaments. In the archaic and classical period the knowledge of metal-working, because of its obvious connection to power and wealth, was preserved in secrecy and handed down in craft-guilds from master to student. Such technical knowledge was regarded as magical by ordinary people, because it seemed to involve inexplicable mastery of natural forces.

A popular misconception is that alchemy was solely and futilely concerned with the transmutation of base metals to gold. In actuality, it is clear from alchemical writings that the main focus of most alchemical practitioners was transformative insight and healing: the transmutation of the physical and psychic condition of the human being – starting with oneself. Alchemists and shamans had specialised knowledge of plants and mineral substances, including crystals, and secret initiatory knowledge of the spiritual dimensions. They negotiated with the normally inaccessible spirits of nature and the ancestors on behalf of their client communities for problem solving, healing and guidance.

Alchemists, like shamans, worked with spirits, in particular the spirits of the elements (air, fire, earth and water) as well as the spirits of animals and plants. In Germanic-Norse mythology, the spirits of stone, metal and fire were called the 'black elves' (*Schwarzalben*) or dwarves. These dwarves were neither benevolent nor malevolent toward humans. They were said to have their own agenda, neutral in regard to human welfare or survival. But one could communicate with them and learn from them, if one knew how to invoke them. We can see in this ancient mythic conception an understanding of the principle that the knowledge of natural forces is morally neutral: it can be used for good, in the service of the Divine and of life; but when used for personal aggrandisement, domination and enrichment at the expense of others, it becomes sorcery, the 'dark side'.

Oversimplifying somewhat, one could say that alchemy and yoga are the Western and Eastern extensions and developments of Paleolithic shamanism respectively: all three are systematic technologies of physico-psychic-spiritual transformation. It appears that in the Indian and Chinese traditions, physical, psychic and spiritual transformation all remained more connected, even although sub-schools and movements arose which focused on one or another aspect. In the West, the psychic and spiritual aspects of human elemental transformation experienced an amazing flowering in the Hermetic traditions which arose in Egyptian, Hellenistic and Arabic lands during the classical era, and flourished well into medieval and Renaissance times in Christian Europe. It was then suppressed, along with astrology, magic and witchcraft (the mostly feminine herbal medicine traditions) during the advent of the scientific, experimental method – leaving only chemistry, divorced from all psychic and spiritual considerations, as the modern inheritor of this ancient holistic science and art.

In the European Middle Ages, because of the persecutory dominance of the Catholic Church, the practices of alchemy and shamanism (called witchcraft – the 'craft of the wise ones') were deliberately shrouded in secrecy, as a kind of protective camouflage. Texts were written and illustrated, but in a symbolic code, the keys to which were largely lost, and which therefore became increasingly garbled. It remained to C.G. Jung and his followers, in the 20th Century, to recover the lost language of alchemy and re-interpret it as referring to psycho-spiritual transformation using symbolic and imaginal processes.

Jung interprets the opus or work of alchemy as being the individuation process – moving toward wholeness. The alchemical vessel, in his view, is the psyche, both individual and interpersonal relational, in which these transformative processes are taking place. From my own studies of alchemical yoga, I would add only that the alchemical vessel should be understood to refer also to the physical body and subtle energy-field, and not merely the mental-emotional psyche. In other words, the entire set of interrelated energy-systems constituting the human being is the vessel in which the alchemical transformations are taking place. The human energy-systems, which can also be thought of as 'personality systems', are the multi-layered vessel, container, body or form for the immortal Soul, Spirit, or Essence.

One difference between modern psychotherapy and the traditional transformation systems is that shamanism, alchemy and yoga are not focussed only on the solving of psychological problems, as is most psychotherapy. Rather, these traditional systems operate from an integrated world-view, in which physical healing, psychological problem-solving, and conscious exploration of spiritual or sacred realms of being are all considered as aspects of the way, or work, or practice. A shamanic ritual such as the Native American sweat-lodge, for example, is simultaneously a healing, a psychological therapy, and a form of worship including prayer. The alchemists' interest in healing is evident in their search for and preparation of plant and mineral remedies. Their deep spiritual commitment is likewise apparent in their quest to produce the lapis, the philosophers' stone, which parallels the tantra yoga idea of the vajra, the lightning-diamond. In yoga, the spiritual purpose, the attainment of higher states of consciousness is paramount and physical or psychological problem-solving is almost a secondary effect.

60

The purpose of psychotherapy on the other hand is not generally to bring about physical healing, nor does it concern itself normally with spiritual values or religious issues. The goal is usually framed in terms of psycho-social adjustment, or the resolution of intrapsychic conflicts, or interpersonal communication problems. The split in the Western worldview between body, mind and spirit is reflected in the rigid separation of the roles of physician, therapist, and priest. There are, however, encouraging signs that this situation may be changing: the contribution of psychological factors to the origins and the treatment of diseases is increasingly acknowledged. The work of C.G. Jung with archetypes, of Abraham Maslow with the notion of self-actualisation, and of Roberto Assagioli with psychosynthesis, has pointed the way toward greater recognition of spiritual factors. The transpersonal psychology movement, for example in the brilliant work of

Stanislav Grof, pioneer of psychedelic and holotropic therapy, explicitly integrates the spiritual dimensions into a comprehensive understanding of the human psyche.

The second important difference in goals and values is that psychotherapy focusses on changing or helping the other – the patient, client, victim, sufferer; whereas in the traditional systems of shamanism, alchemy and yoga, the emphasis is on self-transformation, self-healing, self-understanding. While it is true that the more sophisticated approaches to psychotherapy are well aware of the relevance of the therapist's own perceptions and feelings to the therapeutic process, these tend to be categorised as 'countertransference' reactions, and seen as an impediment to the conduct of therapy, to be eliminated if possible.

On the other hand, while it is also true that helping or healing others is the chief interest and application of shamanic work, such work is always based on the shaman's own preparation and inner process: typically, the healer shaman must contact his or her own power animal or ally, in order to facilitate a similar contact with inner sources of support and healing for the patient or sufferer. The widespread concept of the 'wounded healer' points to a direct personal engagement of the healer with the sickness or wounding of the patient. The shaman may journey into the inner world in order to combat or destroy the 'spirits' or 'forces' that are manifesting as physical or psychic pathology.

61

The comparison of shamanism, alchemy and yoga as traditional systems of consciousness transformation, with modern psychotherapy as a problem-solving approach that uses similar methods and similar metaphors, must be tempered by the awareness that the traditional systems see the human being as an integrated body-mind-spirit continuum. Their approach seeks to recover a way of knowledge that can not only heal and solve psychic problems, but lead to ultimate concerns of human destiny and the meaning of life.

Combining the Sacred & Profane
Threshold HouseBoys Choir
Peter Christopherson

n the 1940 version of the film The Thief of Bagdad, there's a scene in which the teenage Sabu, playing the charming street-boy of the title, is wandering lost in the desert when he sees an ancient encampment materialise in front of him.

Sabu in The Thief of Bagdad

Inside, the unsuspecting lad is welcomed as a Prince, and told that its inhabitants have been waiting two millennia for him to come. The white-bearded old King tells the boy he will inherit everything in his Kingdom, except for one thing – a magic carpet, which the old man is keeping to carry him to Paradise.

Sabu only wants to save his friend who is to be executed in Baghdad at any moment. So, with the old King watching knowingly from shadows, the lad plans to steal the carpet which will carry him there.

Before doing so, he prays to Allah:

'When the old King's hour comes, he won't want a carpet to fly to paradise... Then You, oh Allah, will take him by the hand, gentle and kind as he is, and lead him into eternal Bliss, Aren't I right? Oh Allah, Lord of Justice, let me steal, this one last time... Fly Carpet!'

Of course, the carpet lifts into the air and carries him off to save his friend in the nick of time.

***

The reason I mention this scene is because, in the space of a few short minutes, the storytellers have laid out the beliefs that have shaped my life's work. They are these:

1. That there are forces beyond the human, that take an interest in us, even on occasion, intervening to guide our lives...

2. That society's outcasts, thieves, deviants and prostitutes have as much access to these forces as the rest of us, probably more so. In other words, as you approach the edges of the 'bell curve' of what society considers 'acceptable', only then does the panoply of other worlds beyond this one start to come clearly into view and into reach....

[Though please remember to exercise care when leaning out over the Abyss – the railings round there are well dodgy!]

3. That an open heart, generosity of spirit, even Innocence – not in the Christian moral sense, but in the sense of freedom from an adult's cynicism, greed and 'sophistication' – really goes a long way, when it comes to asking for things from 'Them Upstairs'!

Framed photograph of boy prostitutes with animated LED Buddhist Prayer light. *Copyright Peter Christopherson 2009.*

I live in Thailand, where I believe that for various reasons (both geographical and historical), the tissue that normally separates our everyday world from the other planes of existence is especially thin.

I can tell you from numerous experiences I have had in the last few years that the sight of Thai boy prostitutes (whether dark skinned, tattooed and scary or small and gentle-looking), going to the Temple to make offerings and pray sincerely for one's well-being is enough to tip me over the edge, into a kind of spiritual euphoria at least as strong as any drug I have ever taken (and there have been many), and longer lasting.

It may last forever, for all I know. I hope so. All this life at least.

It is this heady cocktail of both Sacred and Profane, shaken or stirred, that gets me every time.

We are all at our own points on the path to Nirvana. I accept that later I may lose interest in, or rise above, the cravings of earthly desire, or the obsession with Epicurean delights. However, for now I remain captivated by those kids whose wisdom and kindness belies their street level existence, their most ancient and intimate of professions, and their tender years (legal note: 18+ of course!)

65

It is the least I can do in my work, to try to send any Merit I may have accumulated, to them in return...

The Threshold HouseBoys Choir
Brooklyn NY, April 28th 2009.
www.sacred-profane.com

Exploring Your Personal Pantheon:

Gods, Demons
& Imaginary Friends
(whether you believe in them or not)
Philip H. Farber

hen I first began my study of magick, almost thirty years ago, I was fascinated and bewildered by the numerous, often conflicting, systems for cataloguing entities. Every school of thought and every religion offered a pantheon of entities, avatars, teachers, and earthly representatives. Catalogues were filled with icons; pantheons were crowded with gods and goddesses; angels organised in hierarchies more complex than government offices; and demons likewise lined up behind their bigger, badder brethren. Even the most ostensibly monotheistic religions still had lists of saints, prophets, teachers, legendary characters, and further subdivisions of their One True, yet nonetheless divisible, God.

All these systems were fascinating, of course, and I spent many days, weeks, months and years with my nose stuck in Jung's Man and His Symbols, poring over Crowley's 777, spreading tarot cards on my living room floor, tossing coins among the piles of tarot cards, and creating magic marker enneagrams, vévés, and hieroglyphs. I soon found that a few of these entities had the ability to affect me in surprising ways. Some I found I was inexplicably drawn to – I wrote short stories and created tarot cards for the god Pan for many years, formed rituals involving Aleister Crowley's triumvirate of Nuit, Hadit, and Ra-Hoor-Khuit and placed candy, rum and cigars on altars for Voodoo loas, for instance. Some entities similarly repelled me. Most simply did not touch me in any immediately significant way. But ultimately my question about all of these was, 'Why this stuff?' The teaching was that these entities were symbols, archetypes from the collective unconscious, from some dreamworld of Plato's in which the proper shapes of all things were stored.

Now that sounds fine to me. I'm very happy with the idea that our unconscious minds intersect someplace, that we share the common implicit information that is the world beyond our immediate awareness. It makes sense to me on a very practical level – that everything in the universe influences everything else, no matter how slightly or significantly and that, therefore, information about everything is available everywhere, if we have the ability to decode it. That still doesn't offer an answer to how we came up with this particular stuff from among all the potential shapes and forms, gods, angels, demons and symbols of the unperceived world. What is it about that memetic complex that we call a god that makes it a god? How was this stuff first derived? And ultimately – along with understanding the nature of the gods and goddesses from books and esoteric lore that I had come to love – I wanted to find a pantheon within my own life and experience.

After some years of contemplating this issue of the origin of archetypes, I decided that the emphasis on the stuff was only half the equation. The stuff – the names, shapes, clothing and bedroom habits of the gods – represents the content, the collection of ideas and perceptions that we circle in a metaphysical Venn diagram to delineate exactly what constitutes a particular entity. The answer to my question lay as much in the hand that pushes the pen to make the circle – or rather in the mind that guides that hand.

The question now became, 'What is it about a particular collection of stuff that fires off the part of my brain that recognises it as something meaningful?' What makes the character of Ganesh recognisable to worshipers as a god, for instance? It's a more complex question than it might appear on the surface.

The first level to be peeled back deals with how we recognise anything as conscious, as something with which we can communicate. An intuitive Turing Test, if you will, performed by the unconsciousness mind, seems to immediately categorise things into 'conscious entity' and 'inanimate lump.' We look at each other and, hopefully, we recognise another human as both conscious and at least reasonably intelligent. Some very simple visual patterns, for instance, seem to fire off this sense of recognition – a smiley face have-a-nice day symbol is recognisable to us as a human face; a South Park cartoon character can be identified with, at least for a half hour at a time, as a conscious entity with the ability to communicate, make decisions, and act, however stupidly, upon the world. Linguistic patterns also seem to have a similar ability. A sentence formed with proper syntax suggests that its writer or speaker is possessed of some measure of intelligence. Whereas a formed with sentence syntax that proper its suggests little or nothing. Based on such unconscious intuitions, we recognise writers as conscious entities when we read their well-formed sentences. We recognise other humans as such when we communicate with each other in text environments such as Internet forums. And we even recognise fictional characters as entities for whom we might predict behaviour and sympathise. There are likely also many other behavioural patterns and cues that help us to, unconsciously, tell the difference between a conscious entity and a brick of cheese.

This all made much more sense to me when I came across the concept of mirror neurons. These are physical structures in the brain which enable us to build predictive models of intelligence or consciousness. In effect, mirror neurons build models of entities and use our own consciousness as computing power to run those models. We look at another person and we a) recognise them as another person, and b) try them on for size to some degree. This suggests that mirror neurons are not only the operative force behind empathy, sympathy, and most forms of communication, but may also explain some of the phenomena involving gods and demons with which I was struggling.

First, let's demonstrate how mirror neurons work. The following exercises are excerpted from the Maybe Logic Academy self-directed Internet course Altered States: Ecstasy and Invocation (© 2008 Philip H. Farber, used with permission).

Watch Yourself Relax

Imagine that you can see yourself, or hear yourself, or feel yourself, as if observing another person. Make it like looking at a movie or a picture of yourself. If you are better at hearing or feeling, then hear yourself talking or making sounds, or feel where your presence would be.

Imagine that this other self that you are observing is in a place that is very comfortable and very, very relaxing. It's not necessary to see, hear or feel the place, just keep your attention on this other self.

Watch, listen, and/or feel as this other self becomes more and more relaxed, more and more comfortable, and exhibits the effects of relaxation: softer muscles, different posture, different facial expression, and so forth.

Make changes to the structure of the image (but not the content):

Make the image larger or smaller
Make the colors brighter or more muted
Emphasize the foreground as opposed to the background, and vice versa
Make the sounds or speech louder or quieter (if the emphasis is on hearing rather than seeing)
Speed up and slow down the action (works for all senses)
Move the image closer or farther away (works for all senses)
Give the image a soft glow or sparkles
Notice any changes to your state as you experiment with these changes.

Notice that this exercise deals not just with our ability to recognise entity-

hood in our dealings with external stuff, but also with the stuff that we imagine, the dissociated images and entities that we create in our minds. The very stuff that gods, demons, and imaginary friends are made from. Also notice how subtle changes in the structure of that stuff, the alterations we make in the form and quality of our internal image, have the ability to change our response to the entity. Different configurations affect our consciousness in different ways. Making the representation larger or smaller, brighter or dimmer, etc., will often continue the process of making us more or less relaxed. Hopefully you found a configuration that was just wonderfully relaxing.

While that's just an image of you, we're starting to find some clues to the anatomy of entities of any kind. And even better, we may notice some direct connections between the anatomy of an entity and our own states of consciousness.

Let's consider for a moment our criteria for recognising something as god or goddess, demon or angel. There are, generally, two major magical operations that involve these critters: invocation and evocation. Invocation is the drawing into oneself of a quality or entity; evocation is the externalisation of a quality or entity. In a traditional invocation of Hermes, we might visit a temple of Hermes and contemplate his image, or recite a descriptive poem in his honour, or create a magick circle and bring into it only those things of Hermetic nature, so that we might become more Hermetic ourselves. In a traditional evocation we might summon a Goetic spirit into a triangle and question it about what would make life better for us or constrain it to perform some task for us to that same end. We perform these operations quite naturally in daily life, outside the context of magick or mysticism. When we are inspired by another person or a work of art, that is a kind of invocation. When we imagine conversations with people who aren't present, or attempt to verbally convince our computer connection to go faster, we are engaging in mild forms of evocation.

Let's say that, for the purposes of this discussion, our entities become useful when we can use them to perform invocation and evocation willfully and with well-defined intent. An entity suitable for invocation could, ideally, change you in some desired way by contemplating the entity and drawing it into yourself. An entity suitable for evocation would be able to impart information or perform tasks according to your will. In our Meta-Magical explorations, we hope to discover entities in relation to our own states and our consciousness, rather than necessarily learning some previous explorer's version of a pantheon. (And when we all do this, perhaps we'll find that we have many of these entities in common.)

As in the preceding exercise, we begin with an image of the self. Our hypothesis here is that a self image is the very essence of entity-recognition.

It is our basic reference point for consciousness and can also help to reveal our own innate pantheons, the entities who already inhabit our world of consciousness. To change that image from our human self to that of a god, we have to tweak the parameters in order for that image (or voice or feeling) to rise to the level of something useful in invocation or evocation, something with the potential to change us through interaction.

Instant God(dess)

Decide on a quality that you either have and would like to enhance, or one that you don't have and would like to acquire. For instance, creativity, compassion, patience, strength, assertiveness, financial skill, adaptability, understanding, concentration, flexibility, love, sex appeal, or whatever you decide upon. Make sure this quality is a positive one, that is, it is one that stands on its own and is not expressed as a lack of something else (for instance, 'reduced stress' might be expressed here as 'relaxation', 'no more bad luck' might be expressed for these purposes as 'good luck' and so on).

Breathe and banish

Imagine a circle around yourself, at about the diameter of your spread arms. Sit or stand in the center of that circle. Fill your lungs completely, with a slow, even inhalation. As you inhale, allow your attention to expand to fill the circle. As you exhale, slowly, evenly, and completely, allow your attention to contract to a single point in the center of your chest. Repeat at least three times.

Create a dissociated image of yourself (an image, voice or feeling of you as if perceived by another person or in a recording), standing or sitting. Eliminate background and any accessories, objects, props, and so on that might be in your image, so that the image is just you.

Begin to adjust the physiology of the imagined person to include more and more of your desired quality. Pay attention to and adjust facial expression, posture, breathing, movements, skin tone, muscle usage and anything else that might pertain.

Adjust the structure of the image (submodalities) for greater impact. Experiment with image size, colour depth and quality, image location, and special effects such as glows, sparkles, shimmers. Take each of these to its greatest intensity – for instance, the image could be increased to much greater than life-size. If this image were a god of that particular quality, how would these submodalities manifest? Just how big, bright, loud, strong and sparkly is a god(dess) of x?

Begin to add in extra features and aspects from other humans, from animals, machines as appropriate to a god(dess) of this quality. For instance, if cunning and strength are useful to this entity, give it some qualities of a tiger or other animal that might represent those qualities (head, body, teeth, eyes, whatever). If enhanced intelligence or processing speed is important, then maybe a computer chip or having a computer as an accessory might work. Take as much time as is necessary to test out some of these qualities. Notice which ones feel the best and keep them. Have fun with this and make your image fantastic.

Adjust physiology to account for the additions. If you added a computer chip to the brain, how would that be reflected in facial expression, breathing, posture, etc.? Contemplate the image for at least 30 seconds.

Pull the image into the circle with you and draw it into you. Wear it like clothing, wrap it around you, let it interpenetrate your body and mind. Let your own body, posture, breathing, facial expression, etc. reflect what you saw in this image. Let the memories of this (future) self who has already resolved this basic need be your memories. Breathe and banish. Be open to thoughts, epiphanies, and suggestions from your unconscious mind that may occur throughout the day as a result of this practice.

Now, these exercises are offered here for demonstration purposes, to give some practical experience of the relationship between entities and consciousness. For the most part, entities produced or contacted in this way are personal ones, not necessarily god or goddess archetypes familiar to us from the astral storehouse of sacred images. However, sometimes they do rise to that level and first-time practitioners occasionally find themselves face-to-face with deities who offer names and abilities drawn from known pantheons and belief systems.

The sample exercises offered here demonstrate an extremely stripped-down and basic mode of working. There are endless modifications and enhancements to these processes of deriving personal pantheons from our unconscious minds. At some point, they become much more than simple demonstrations of a point – but I'll leave that, for now, to your own imagination and experience.

(And before you're off to read the next piece, I'll just note that to fully understand the point that this article dances around, no matter how well you think you get it on an intellectual level, it is most likely necessary to actually perform the experiments. You have to look through the microscope and adjust the focus before you really know what a micro-organism is like. And it likewise helps to change the focus of your mind before you really understand the nature of the entities all around us, including gods, goddesses, demons, angels, imaginary friends, ideologies, corporations, schools of art, mass movements and those mysterious bipeds we call 'human').

I come through the g a p s,
when the expected is averted.
For I am Fate,
Beyond the intent of the individual
At least, oft Beyond hir conscious will,
Yet aligned with hir True Will

If the Magickian be nimble and True,
He can twist and dance with Fate's strike,
And see the Greater stakes
Beyond the expected extant course

For my apparent cruelty
Is but the mask of the Mother
Who knows the best for Her children
Beyond the immediate

Focus not on a single strand
Failing to see the whole weave
For She whom doth from TimemiT
Knows its full course

And the Pattern of the Greater Web

We're the Earth with *Spirit,*
We're the Earth with *Soul*
Z'EV

ANIMISIM:

he belief that each and every natural phenomena and object: such as stones, trees, the wind and etc., and every dream and idea too, are individually alive and possessing of Spirit.

The following writing was greatly inspired by an audiotape I happened upon entitled *Fate of the Earth*, which documents a lecture delivered by Sister Miriam Theresa MacGillis.

Her speech that day cast a beautiful lumination on the edited version of the following quote by Plutarch that appeared in the opening pages of his book, *On the Cessation of the Oracles*: 'Often the body all by itself attains the condition of enthusiasm, but the Earth (emphasis mine) sends up to human beings the sources of many faculties other than this, some of which produce Trance'

Note that the Greek word enthusiasm can be translated as 'possession' or 'inspiration'. This is maybe closer to what we mean by our word 'ecstasy', itself borrowed from the Greek *ekstasis* whose actual translation is 'stepping outside oneself'.

In his book, Coming to Our Senses: body and spirit in the hidden history of the West, Morris Berman distinguishes two world views – the vertical and the horizontal. Verticality is clearly the view adopted by Non-Animistic cultures, with their love of hard-edged differences and hierarchies, and especially in their 'exterior' concept of the dynamics of transcendence. In contrast, the horizontal view involves a continuum of interpenetrating relationships and experience, a view obviously held by Animistic cultures. And this view also allows for 'interior' as opposed to 'exterior' modes of sacred experience.

So this vertical view of transcendence helped to create the Non-

Animistic paradigm in which our beautiful world is simply material. Within this paradigm the Earth is emphatically not involved in the process of the human interacting with the divine. Granted, the Earth was seen as a reflection of the divine, and so could be seen as potentially holy, but it was not spirit. No way. It was material.

So while the notion of a Mother Nature still exists for most Non-Animistic peoples, it has long been relegated to being just a figure of speech. It is no longer absolutely the Earth Mother who gave birth to them, nurtured them, stood beside them, and is waiting to take them back.

Paradoxically however, the roots of this view go back some 6-8000 years ago, to the period when the great mother-goddesses ruled supreme. For it was the development of agriculture in Mesopotamia, Egypt, the Indus Valley, and China that instigated the shift from the horizontal/animistic view of the hunter-gatherer to the hierarchical/vertical view of the farmer. This expansion of agriculture was easily achieved because the farmers' knowledge was not tied to a particular patch of land as the hunter-gatherers' had been.

For farmers colonisation was easy, because they knew how to transform systematically any piece of land into a farm. Unfortunately this expansion proceeded into land already occupied by the ancient hunter-gatherer communities, and this began the conflict between two fundamentally different views of the land. The hunters saw their land as a place to which they were attached, like the trees that grew from it. To the farmers land was property, not a place. It was a 'thing' to own. To buy, to sell and subdivide. And the hunter-gatherers were simply outnumbered. Twenty comparatively malnourished farmers could always overcome one healthy hunter.

It is this perception of an objectified and 'material' world that enabled Non-Animistic peoples to evolve a very real and very literal detachment and abstraction from the Earth, and worse, an arrogance whereby they felt they had dominion over it. And it was that very selfsame sense of detachment and obsession with abstraction that enabled Non-Animistic culture and her science to put nature on the rack and force her to give up her secrets. This translates as observing her purely physical and mechanistic attributes and functions, the practical applications of which allowed for the development of what Non-Animists so proudly call their technology.

This 'objectifying nature' of science could be seen to have its roots in agriculture as well. The bastions of science then, mathematics and writing, can both be seen to have been outgrowths of agriculture: the measuring of land was necessary for the division of properties, and the measurement of amounts, seeds or grains, was also a factor in farming.

As the small fixed agricultural communities evolved into cites, the institution of measurements and the attendant notions of value and currency would have evolved as well. Measurement, commodity, value and currency all required some form of record keeping, naturally leading to that most paramount of abstractions – writing. Paramount because, in no way imaginable is the written word the thing.

In his article *Resonant Media*, Marshall Soules writes:

'Only alphabetic cultures have ever succeeded in mastering connected linear sequences as a means of social and psychic organisation; the separation of all kinds of experiences into uniform and continuous units in order to generate accelerated action and alteration of form – in other words, applied knowledge – has been the secret of Western man's ascendancy over other men as well as over his environment.'

I would read dominance in place of ascendancy here myself. And so it was this same fetish for abstraction and technology, and its elevation to a maybe only semi-divine status, that allows the Non-Animist to think they also have dominion over Animistic, or what they generally refer to as pre-technical, cultures.

Now this is very different from Animistic cultures.

For them, their divine creative force suffused a multiverse that was no different from the Earth, and because they believed that, it followed that the Earth was an actual 'presence'. This paradigm was what determined how they evolved their concepts of sanctity and their manners of worshipping and maintaining their contact with the divine. And that maintaining was what determined how they shaped their moral, ethical and economic systems.

Because every thing reflected in a concrete, incarnate way the essence of the divine that manifested through that thing, be it an animal, vegetable, mineral, element, thought, idea or disembodied force of nature.

In direct contrast to this, the Non-Animistic cosmology enabled its adherents to take what they thought of as the last dense piece of matter, that is the atom, and learn how to split it apart. And since that time more and more people have come to realise that the dominant and dominating Non-Animistic world view that we live under can no longer underpin the world culture if we – and this includes the Earth and all of her inhabitants – are to survive.

Because, as Big Science has probed the interior of the atom, it has been faced with the fact that its whole paradigm of what's real – a reality totally dependant upon and invested in materiality – dissolves. Because even a simple vision/version of reality is just not measurable, nor simply quantifiable. Because what's real can either be a particle or a wave, a this or a that, depending on the observer. Because, in fact, mirrored in the depths of the atom are very deep Spiritual and Psychic inner dimensions.

So the Non-Animistic paradigm of a totally physical uni-verse to exercise dominion over, simply has to be replaced with that of a transforming and transformative multi-verse. For a multi-verse is a process. And not only a process, but also a process with deep and wide spiritual interiors that are expanding and unfolding, as they have been, over aeons of Time.

In fact however, we, Animists and Non-Animists alike, are only a very recent occurrence in a process which Big Science says began some 15 billion years ago with the emergence of hydrogen. So some 15 billion years ago an event took place. The 'big bang' of Big Science or the 'shattering of the vessels' of the qabalhists, or whichever is your favorite. (My personal favorite is Wilhelm Reich's notion of 'cosmic superimposition'.) Anyway, an event took place out of which the hydrogen atom emerged.

But it seems that for only some seven seconds were those hydrogen atoms alone. Because out of an infolding of hydrogen atoms came the unfolding of helium. And then out of the unfolding of helium atoms infolded the unfolding of carbon. And once you have those three differentiated elements in place; the physical universe, as we know it, can begin to infold and unfold to greater and greater levels of complexity.

Now as Big Science has just so relatively recently discovered,within the hydrogen atom are spaces so vast that they are literally immeasurable. So not only does the universe unfold externally, but internally as well there is an unfolding towards greater and greater complexities of potential. And the permutations of all these possible potentials manifest in-and-as what I am referring to as the multiverse.

In his book, *The Infinity Concerto*, Greg Bear puts this concept quite nicely:

'Analogous to the groove in a phonograph record, which is easily distinguished into horns and strings by the practiced ear – horns one universe, strings another... A universe, a world, (a life) is just one long difficult song.... The difference between worlds is (like) the difference between songs'

So. By the time our sun came into being some five billion years ago in this process, and with our Sun our Solar System, there were atomic elements capable of becoming the heavy metals which eventually formed the crust of the Earth. So let's take that five billion years and compress it into the framework of twelve months and then we can hopefully get a totally new take on the unfolding of the potential of what Ms. Miriam calls; the 'Fate of the Earth'.

So it would have taken the Earth about eight months of this hypothetical year to create – through an almost unbelievably coincidentally unbroken sequence of events – the conditions that enabled the Earth's crust to foldingly form, the oceans to fallingly form; those same oceans out of which all life forms emerged, and thus are indebted to... And then the original mass of what we now call land was shaped into the Ur-continent sometimes called Gowandaland, which would itself eventually break up and then eventually redistribute itself over the surface of the Earth.

And all of this in three-quarters of our allotted year. For during this time too came the development of the complex biological structures that created the conditions necessary for the emergence of amino acids. Amino acids that themselves were coded and encoded and came together to form a total of just 20 proteins from out of which life, as we know it, was able to unfold. Then we come back to hydrogen because, and this should maybe come as no surprise, hydrogen bonds are what hold the bases of the two strands of DNA together to form their double helix.

So this life-as-we-know-it unfolded on the Earth, relatively, about four months ago. And then out of that process, in terms of an accelerating of genetic complexity... the permutating chains of amino acid proteins... the Earth began, in what has to be seen as a most extraordinary way, to express herself through life, beginning with simple bacteria, plankton, and multi-celled algae.

And then between some 570 and 530 million years ago the 'Cambrian explosion' took place. This event takes its name from the geological age in whose early part it occurred. It was during this 40-some million year evolutionary flowering of multicellular life that the genetic phylum/ lineages of almost all animals living today began to unfold out of her gene pool. And they began and continued to evolve and continue even still, although not one new phylum has emerged since this event.

And in the face of this teeming multitude of life the Earth, in her inner spiritual and psychic dimensions, is becoming more and more capable of expressing her spiritual dimension. For she becomes capable of ever-greater forms of expression as her exterior material dimensions evolve.

And with regard to the expressions of those dimensions, we only have to look as far as the magnetosphere, or aura, of the Earth for one example. The magnetosphere is the volume between the Earth's outer ionosphere and her crust. It is charged by the magnetic field generated by her spin, and by the interaction with that field of the plasma waves coming from throughout the Solar System and the wider cosmos. And, shaped by geomagnetism, Earth's organisms evolved not only in air and water but in this electromagnetic environment. Until recently, scant attention has been paid to magnetism in evolution, but there are now suggestions that the evolution of life has been closely related to the behaviour of the Earth's magnetic field.

Strong correlations between times of abrupt physical and cultural changes in man and reversals of the earth's magnetic field [the switching of the poles] have noted. Two examples of this are: the Blake excursion, c. 114,000 - 108,000 BCE, which coincides with the disappearance of Lower Paleolithic tools and the appearance of Middle Paleolithic tools and Neanderthals; and the Mungo excursion, c. 37,000 - 32,000 BCE, which coincides with the Middle/Upper Paleolithic boundary and the replacement of neanderthals by Cro-Magnons.

So to return to our on-going story, if we trace the last four months of our hypothetical year of life on the Earth, it was during this time-period that her efforts in the unfolding of complexity and diversification and evolution were rewarded with organisms so complex that she was now capable of thinking about herself as well. And, well, that includes the higher level mammals, of which humans are but one member.

So in our deepest definition, and in our deepest subjectivity: humans are the Earth. And so there's maybe no coincidence then that both the Earth's surface and the human body are both approximately 60 per cent liquid. So, for better or worse, we are beings in-and-by whom the

Earth experiences, reflects and, most of all, remembers.

So let's pause and consider that, relative to this time frame, humanity has only been around for one day. One day. And the majority of that time – 23 and a half hours– was spent in the great Tribal Age that vastly predates even what we would call ancient history (20 thousand years by the most conservative of estimates). And now, in the last few moments of the remaining 30 minutes ; the Earth is approaching another other level of her evolution.

And this level is being reflected in the we who are the Earth's thoughts. The developments of the last 100 years like the ecology movement, like holistic health, like the 'consciousness revolution' and all the so-called New Age or New Edge or New What-Evers; these came to us through her. They came to us through a reciprocity that is just beginning to unfold.

and how do we help her unfold?
through listening to Her
and how can we listen to Her
through the Trance state
for She speaks to us
in that soft inner voice
beating throughout our bodies
through the Trance state.

And, as a practitioner, I truly believe entering the Trance state fundamentally heals not only the individual but the Earth as well.

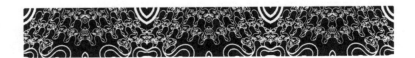

Beelzebub - Barry William Hale

Remember Mugwort,
what you made known:
Mugwort (Artemesia vulgaris),
The Nine Herbs Charm and 'New Animism'

Robert J. Wallis

ugwort is an easily overlooked plant whose grey feathery leaves grace roadside verges and 'wasteground' across Britain. Writes EA Armstorng in 1944: 'It is not pretty, nor even conspicuous, and it is remarkable that it should ever have attained to fame and sanctity'. That it is named in a very deliberate manner in the Old English 'Nine Herbs' charm attests in part to the special status ascribed by Armstrong some fifty years hence. Folklore associates Mugwort (Artemesia vulgaris) with fair journeying and inspired dreams: for the former, the traveller should carry Mugwort leaves, or perhaps eat one or two to relieve fatigue; for the latter, one might sleep with a small bundle of leaves under one's pillow, or drink an infusion of the leaves before retiring to bed. Armstrong also tells us:

'In the Isle of Man…it was gathered on Midsummer Eve 'as a preventative against the influence of witchcraft' and placed in chaplets and the heads of man and beast to ward off evil influences. In France… it is worn to prevent aches and pains. In Germany, the people had like customs and eventually threw the girdles and crowns of Mugwort into the Midsummer fire. In East Prussia it was used for divination. At Midsummer Artemesia alba is used as a fumigant in Morocco.'

Mugwort may derive part of its name – mug – from being used, among such other herbs as Ground Ivy, to flavour drinks, especially beer before the introduction of hops. (My own experiments indicate that research on Mugwort-flavoured beer might be most perspicacious.) Alternatively, 'Mugwort' may be derived from moughte ('moth' or 'maggot'), as an insect repellent or attractant, thanks to its acting as

82

a host plant for a number of moth species, including Odontopera bidentata (Scalloped Hazel), Amphipyra tragopoginis (Mouse Moth), Antitype chi (Grey Chi), Eupithecia succenturiata (Bordered Pug), Chloroclystis v-ata (V-Pug), Bucculatrix noltei, Coleophora artemisicolella and Coleophora trochilella.

Mugwort's chemical composition is of some interest. It contains 'ethereal oils' such as cineole and thujone. Cineole or 'wormwood oil', related to eucalyptol, can reduce inflammation and pain, and clinical trials show effectiveness against the symptoms of sinusitis. Thujone has a reputation by virtue of its significantly active presence in absinthe, thought to give the drink its 'hallucinogenic' properties by affecting cannabinoid receptors in the brain in a similar way to Tetrahydrocannabinol (THC).

While the molecular shapes are similar, thujone actually acts as a Gamma-aminobutyric acid (GABA) receptor antagonist, so that neurons may fire more easily, resulting – in high doses – in muscle spasms and convulsions. Thujone may also help regulate menstruation, but caution is required: at said higher doses, it may act as an abortifacient (causing miscarriage). Other constiuents of Mugwort include flavonoids (antioxidants), triterpenes (resins), and coumarin (an anticoagulant and derivative of the blood-thinning drug warfarin) derivatives. According to herbal medicine, chewing some leaves reduces fatigue and stimulates the nervous system, it has been used as an anthelminthic (a vermifuge, expelling worms from the body), has stimulant and slightly tonic properties, and works as a nervine, emmenagogue, diuretic and diaphoretic. Mugwort is also used in traditional Chinese medicine in the form 'moxa' for moxibustion (an external heat and smoke treatment).

Mugwort leaves are used as incense, and I find that the smoke is pleasantly sweet, not dissimilar from Sage or Cannabis in the form of 'grass'. In her study on seidr practices (past and present), *Nine Worlds of Seidr Magic*, Jenny Blain mentions a number of indigenous entheogens which may have been recognised as such in the Old North, addressing Mugwort's effects, however, as 'mild if there at all'. She notes the importance of 'set and setting', as Leary and others have described it, 'in evaluating the effects of mind-altering substances', seemingly indicating that while Mugwort's effects are apparently mild, a particular mood and environment might accentuate the potential effects. My experiments, involving smoking the leaves under 'ritual' circumstances, indicate this is indeed the case. These experiments involve walking to my local 'sacred sites', respecting the wights of the place via an offering (usually of alcohol), honouring certain deities with galdor and further offerings, 'sitting-out' – and putting a number of dried Mugwort leaves (usually nine, that sacred number of the North), crushed into a ball, into my pipe. Having learned a number of stanzas of 'The Nine Herbs Charm', in Old English and in translation, I recite these in honour of the plant, addressing its 'spirit', and proceed to smoke the pipe.

The smoke is grey, as the underside of the leaves, and dissipates quickly. It fires easily, burns readily, stays alight with ease, and burns to a black and white ash with the leaf-shape in tact. The scent is floral, closest to 'grass' – tasting sweet initially, followed by a pleasant, nutty aftertaste. Within a few moments of inhalation, I experience an immediate feeling of being 'captured' by the plant, an 'arresting' of attention, though this is too strong a word. There is, rather, a stillness, a focusing of concentration, focused in the eyes, and visual attention is brought forward. My body feels suddenly relaxed, in total stillness, with a seething in the knees and neck. I am reminded positively of the fact that I am alive, and feel attuned to my immediate surroundings. My sense is that Mugwort enjoys to be smoked and this aligns with reports that the plant likes to be used as incense.

84

As time passes, I experience a strong euphoria, a great joy at being in place, among green things, living things. The indication is that Mugwort likes to be smoked among other plants, as if attuning to them, and communing with other plant-people – 'is it speaking through me?' I have thought: one might think the plant is a conduit to communing with place, but it might be that human-people act as vessels for the plant to communicate, in a sort of 'possession'. After a few moments, my eyelids become a little heavy, a feeling again reminiscent of cannabis, albeit with less of an active mind. It is not that I feel like sleeping, I just feel relaxed, as if among friendly company in this alive environment. It is a very friendly feeling and Mugwort is in no way harsh – in smoke, in flavour, in intent, in effect. An otherworldy glow, hue or fuzziness comes to vision; as such, Mugwort offers a certain experience of otherworldliness, of being in an altered place/space. As a scryer I find that smoking Mugwort intensifies my experience visually, focussing vision in certain ways. After around half-an-hour, the brightness of the experience fades and I feel more sleepy, and after fifty minutes or so, the effects are gone. My night's sleep following the smoking ritual tends to be at least a little fitful, suggesting scope for dream work. I have also found a strong tea of the leaves highly soporific.

Mugwort is not as intense a mind-alterant as better-known entheogens, but the shift in consciousness is profound nonetheless, even if the measured effects aren't quite so impressive. But frustratingly my description is leaning towards that of the psychonaut, newage-shaman or psychologist – assuming that the 'plant' Mugwort is valuable only for its 'active constituents', as a resource that can be 'used' to alter consciousness. In a sense this is true, but the language is limiting, the impetus disrespectful, and the discourse is not mindful of the intention of the plant itself, its agency, its personality. Such agency has been at the core of my experience, and it is 'made known' also in the attention afforded to Mugwort in 'The Nine Herbs Charm'.

This charm originates in the 'MS London British Library Harley 585' manuscript, named *Lacnunga* ('Remedies', according to Cockayne). 'Approximately the size of a modern paperback' , this 'book', was perhaps 'a general practitioner's travelling reference work' according to RI Page. Jonathan Roper addresses the status of this 'practitioner', noting that 'wise man' or 'wise woman' was an enduring term for a charmer; also 'cunning'. In Old English we also have the terms 'conjurer', 'wizard', and even 'doctor'.

'The Nine Herbs Charm' begins by immediately addressing Mugwort:

'Remember mugwort what you made known / what you set out in mighty revelation / una you are called oldest of herbs / you have might against three and against thirty / you have might against venom and against flying shots / you have might against the loathsome thing that fares around the land...' (Author's translation)

With the consistent use of a personal pronoun, the second-person 'you', Mugwort is clearly being spoken to as if it were a 'person'. This has some significance for our understanding of Anglo-Saxon worldviews. Scholars have often described Anglo-Saxon paganism as a form of 'animism', but this term is deeply problematic. The 'old animism', as presented by the nineteenth century English anthropologist Edward Tylor, assumed that indigenous peoples were mistaken in their belief in 'spirits' and that 'inanimate objects' had 'souls'. This is how Archbishop Wulfstan presented *deofolgyld* ('idolotry') in the law written during Cnut's reign (1016-1035):

'Heathendom is worshipping devil-idols, that is to say the worshipping of heathen gods and sun and moon, fire or flood, water wells or stones or forest-trees of any kind, or the loving of witchcraft or the committing of murders in any way, either in sacrifice or from bringing into fear, or doing anything so deluded as this'.

'The Nine Herbs Charm' offers a tantalising glimpse into Anglo-Saxon animism. But this data and such interpretation as it stands is inadequate: the meaning alludes to 'spirits in things' but tells us nothing of the implications of this, of what 'spirits' are, of what people actually 'did' in their day-to-day lives; indeed, it might even hint that such animic 'beliefs' were 'superstitious' and 'ignorant'.

More recently, scholars such as Nurit Bird-David, Carlos Fausto, Graham Harvey and Eduardo Viveiros de Castro, have examined the sophisticated nature of animic relational ontologies, a 'new animism' redressing Tylor's 'old'. For animists, the world is filled with 'persons' only some of whom are human. An ongoing system of relationships and regulated behaviour steers engagements between human persons and such 'other-than-human-persons' as tree-people, bird-people and stone-people. Human-people often labelled 'shamans' act as mediators, working to maintain harmony between humans and nonhumans: if a hunter offends an animal by using inappropriate etiquette, so resulting in the hunter falling sick, a shaman negotiates between the offended 'spirit' of the dead animal in order to return the stolen 'soul' of the hunter and so restore social harmony between the affected 'persons'. It is important to note that an Anglo-Saxon animism, if such a thing existed, would be culture-specific: we should expect there to be substantial difference between Amazonian, Ojibwe, Maori and Old English animism, even if such a construction as 'tribal' is deemed to be shared between them.

86

One small article can only do so much justice to a topic and there is much scope for further analysis – and debate. The personhood of eight other herbs in 'The Nine Herbs Charm', alongside the appearance of Woden and an adder, as well as 'glory twigs', and the 'flying shots' often associated with elves, may be rich in animistic material. The concluding section to the charm:

'I alone know the running streams / and they enclose nine adders / let all weeds now spring up as herbs / seas slide apart, all salt water / as I blow this poison from you' (Author's translation) hints animically at the flow and regulation of supernatural potency, pertaining to esoteric plant lore, 'shamanic' healing, and the social status and efficacy of the 'leech' (healer/shaman).

I am not suggesting that the ancient sources are essentially heathen with a veneer of Anglo-Saxon Christianity, or vice versa; the situation is more complex, with the recorders of the data (such as charms) clearly Christian but, as North has argued, 'bound by the conventions of a formulaic Anglian vocabulary which was as yet unsuited to [Christian] theological discourse'. As such, heathen discourse is ever-present. Roper suggests that 'traditional verbal charming would appear to be extinct in England' – yet regarding contemporary heathen practice, this short essay marks an example of the revival of English verbal charming, in the form of a re-interpretation of one of the oldest of Anglo-Saxon charms. In place of a 'now-defunct' English charming tradition, this and other active, innovative reconstructionist engagements with the past, suggests, rather, a dynamic and creative heathen tradition.

References:

Armstrong, E.A. 1944. Mugwort Lore. Folklore 55(1): 22-27.

Blain, J. 2002. Nine Worlds of Seid-Magic: Ecstasy and Neo-shamanism in North European Paganism. London: Routledge.

North, R. 1997. Heathen Gods in Old English Literature. Cambridge: Cambridge University Press.

Page, R.I. 1998. Review of 'Popular Religion in Late Saxon England'. The Journal of Ecclesiastical History 49(1): 162.

Roper, J. (ed.) 2004. Charms and Charming in Europe. Basingstoke, Hampshire: Palgrave Macmillan.

Roper, J. 2005. English Verbal Charms. Folklore Fellows Communications 136, no. 288. Helsinki: Suomalainen Tiedeakatemia/Academia Scientiarum Fennica.

A longer version of this article appeared in the Association of Polytheist Traditions Many Gods, Many Voices, *Issue 5, 2008.*

Dreams of Hyperborea –
Krist, Sun of God

David Beth, Fraternitas Borealis

'Should ever that taming talisman break – the Cross – then will come roaring back the wild madness of the ancient warriors, with all their ... Berserker rage, of whom our Nordic poets speak and sing. That talisman is now already crumbling, and the day is not far off when it shall break apart entirely.' Heinrich Heine.

or the first time now it has been decided to make publically available a paper of a mysterious magical and esoteric group called the Fraternitas Borealis. Today this organisation of women and men works internationally under the German 'Hochmeister' David Beth, who is also a leading adept in the O.T.O.A./L.C.N. of Michael Bertiaux and the Ecclesia Gnostica Aeterna.

Although we do not want to explain the history of the order at this point, we will however state some interesting facts. This group was formed in Germany in the latter half of the 19th Century. The founders were, apart from being deeply involved in the pagan/heathen and esoteric/occult traditions (of Germany), also very close to what is know as *Naturphilosophie* and *Lebensphilosophie*. It will suffice for our purpose to mention the close connection of the Order to Ludwig Klages, Alfred Schuler and the Cosmic Circle (*Kosmiker-Kreis*). We also know of a possible direct connection to C.G. Jung through people from the boheme *Schwabing-Ascona* axis.

The initiates of the F.B. have never openly discussed their work, nor have they ever published anything outside the organisation. For good reason, as their idea of occult and magical work was closely tied in with secrecy and arcana. New initiates were 'recruited' only and never by advertising for members. The Order has always strongly opposed the reign of qunatity. Secrecy became even more important after the occult and magical scene, especially in its pagan and volkish shape, became more and more obsessed with profane physical ideas of race which was never the idea or focus of the F.B..

Far from being a typical volkish organization, the F.B. was never interested in defining or creating a physical master race through dividing into physical races or similar ideas. Instead it was concerned with the metaphysical and universal creation of an *Übermensch* utilising the occult, magical and initiatic tools that had been handed down to their initiates via the hyperborean and thus esoteric northern tradition. It was, and is, a universal gnostic magical tradition. 'Hyperboreans' as defined in the F.B. system are a mental 'race' of *Übermenschen*, independent of profane racial heritage such as 'Aryan' or 'Slavic' etc.

In fact members of the Order are of a very diverse racial background, united in an aristocracy of the soul and spirit. As in the system of Esoteric Voudon of Michael Bertiaux, anyone who has the potential to connect to and utilise the current will be able to work within the F.B. and bring to full radiation the mystical *Blutleuchte* (blood-lamp/glow) within himself.

A central mystical force behind all our work is what the philosopher and metaphysicist Ludwig Klages has so adequately termed the 'kosmogonic eros', the world-creating eros that has so little to do with sentimental love or profane eroticism.

The following is a recent paper written for use in the F.B.

Krist-Sun of God

We are an order of male and female warriors. We adhere to the ethos of ancient hyperborean warrior-priesthood as related to us by our ancestors. Courage, honour, sacrifice, loyalty and respect for nature are all integral parts of this way of life. We are in principle a solar community and thus our myths are in accord with this. Solar in our system is not meant to signify the male principle per se. We are not interested in either keeping a patriarchical system or world, nor are we interested in re-establishing a maternal cult. We know that only the fusion of both into a symbiotic system can bring about the new golden age which will follow this age of the wolf. Solar whorship is the only rational and scientifically logical whorship, as the sun is the giver of life. Our ancestors knew this and it is time to recognise it and utilise the magical powers contained within it. We are solar not only because we connect to nature and the life-giving fire of the physical sun, but also because we acknowledge and carry the secrets and mysteries of the *Sol Niger*, the Black Sun, a mysterium so multilayered that we have no time to discuss it here.

There is much debate whether the figure of Christ has a place in our mysteries. The simple answer is that it does very much – in the form of the Solar Krist, the Sun of God. In our school, the Christ myth is closely asscociated not with sun-whorship in its primitive form, but with an elaborate transfer and absorption of solar qualities into the Krist-figure, thus creating a powerful god image and egregor befitting our work as alchemical sexual magicians and warrior-monks.

From the beginning of Christology, this true relating of Krist with the sun was only done in a few sects of gnostics, all descending from and thus working in the ancient hyperborean tradition. We find them in the Ophidian gnostic serpent cults like La Couleuvre Noire who, by equating Christ with the Sun related him also to Damballah and Leghba. He is thus the mighty Sun God at the crossroads. A magical formula of application enables the ophidian sex magicians to draw upon all the magic done in the Christ name and to transfer its power to their rites. All the psychic energy generated by the faithful in Christ is stored in a vast astral reservoir which then can be tapped into by the sex-magicians, who use the energy for the empowerments of their rites.

The same was done by secret esoteric solar Germanic cults, open to male and female members, who were and are in close spiritual relationship with cults of the above-mentioned nature. These Germanic magicians transformed the image of Christ that was presented to them and infused it with all the qualities of their ancient pagan belief system, thus turning him into a powerful warrior-lord embodying the virtues and secret powers of the ancient gods.

A great example of this is found in one of the earliest christian poems in the corpus of Anglo Saxon literature, *The Dream of the Rood*. In the poem, the poet describes his dream of a conversation with the wood of the True Cross. Jesus is portrayed as the heroic model of a Germanic warrior, who faces his death and ultimate blood sacrifice unflinchingly and even eagerly, thus being turned into the solar Krist, bravely going to his death to fight and overcome the forces of darkness, which represent death. In this sense, Krist can be seen as Ingui and perhaps as Donar (Thor), fighting forces of darkness and chaos. The Cross – the Heathen and Germanic early Christian faiths saw the spirit of God running through all things, even a wooden cross – speaking as if it were a member of Krist's band of retainers, accepts its fate as it watches its Creator die, and then explains that Krist's death was not a defeat but a victory. A perfect example of the Germanic-Hyperborean ideal of (blood) sacrifice and esoteric death and cruxifiction on the cross of the elements, followed by the kosmic resurrection as taught in the Fraternitas Borealis.

Some scholars of *The Dream of the Rood* have asserted that the Cross is feminine, and shares a close, almost sexual relationship with the ultra-masculine Krist. The fact that the Cross asserts that the Romans tortured 'unc butu ætgædere' (us both, together) points to a close personal and symbiotic relationship between the Cross and Krist. Where academics scratch the surface, to us initiates this has been clear always, and we know the precise sexual magical formula that lies behind this scholarly assumption. In fact it relates to a powerful mystery of the Cross and the Krist which is closely related to another hyperborean sexual mystery, that of the Soror Mystica. The Anglo-Saxon poem concludes with the poet's prayer to the Rood that he might enter into the band of Krist's followers, like a true knight.

To the Germanic initiates the cross became the Kristianised version of their concept of the cosmos, it represented the World Tree, the Irminsul. The God Wotan (Odin), like Krist, sacrificed himself on a tree (the cross is often referred to as a tree) and was given neither food nor drink. His side was pierced with a spear just like Krist and by undergoing this trial and passing through Hel, the realm of the dead, he symbolically died and in true gnostic fashion was reborn in a more advanced spiritual and physical state.

Through the Cross, Wotan-Krist symbolically passes out of this world and into paradise/pleroma. First though, he descends into Hel and takes the souls of the damned up to heaven with him, bringing them into wholeness and equality with God. The cross is therefore a sort of gateway between this world and the other worlds that lie beyond our human perception. By descending into Hel, Wotan-Krist overcomes death and the forces of darkness. In dying and being reborn he returns to the Father and sits on the throne of the father within all time and space, and this is precisely what we aim at and achieve in our work.

There is a shamanistic hyperborean solar rite in which the initiate utilises a near-death experience to travel to alternate realities and alternate universes. The initiate (as Wotan) undergoes this experience, to the very brink of death, in order to gain insight into the nature of the cosmos. Yet this quest is for more than just wisdom and understanding. By journeying through Hel and into the core of the cosmos we, the initiates, are being joined to it through the ever-flowing web of Wyrd.

In other words, we are able to transcend time and space and to be in all places and all times at once. And after the ultimate rite and the ultimate sacrifice, the hyperoborean initiate of our tradition is all-seeing and all-knowing, not just because he has gained the profound wisdom and understanding of the universe, but because he exists within that wisdom and understanding.

92

In these magical mysteries of the Solar Krist lay great secrets. They show how certain cults, working in the hyperborean, solar tradition, are able to use the Krist-power and have an advantage over all other systems in the world, by viewing and using the solar myth from its most correct esoteric and magical perspective.

Note: An edited version of this essay appeared in Oracle *magazine No. 8.1*

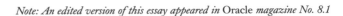

Iä! Shub-Niggurath! – Raymond Salvatore Harmon

Key Baye Fall

Paola Igliori

n 2007 I went to Senegal, finally fulfilling a childhood longing. The first day I arrived I discovered the Baye Fall Confraternity. The first thing that struck me when I arrived at the guest house were two striking hooded figures painted on a wall. One was in black with long dreadlocks and the other in white.

When I asked who they were, the owner of the guest house answered: 'Amadou Bamba and Mame Cheik Ibrahim Fall, the founder of the Baye Fall confraternity to which I belong.'

In the 1870s the French colonialists were relentlessly organising the assimilation of the West African tribes, setting people against each other in an attempt to eradicate their identities. The only defiant presence against this predator spirit was Amadou Bamba.
Imprisoned and exiled for 7 years, Bamba kept his powerful voice through severe trials; he was seen unperturbed, in deep prayer, by his torturers; thrown in the water, he was seen kneeling upon it; put in a room with a lion that had been starved for days, he kept his utmost tranquility while writing a poem. It is said that the lion so sensed this deep peace that it came and knelt in front of him, putting its head on his knees.

Eventually the French brought Bamba in exile to Mayumba in Gabon. Failing to break his spirit, they finally released him under close surveillance. In 1882 he founded the Holy City of Touba.

The ascetic Mame Cheik Ibrahim Fall, who had long sought out Bamba, dedicated his life to the holy man, bringing his powerful spiritual practice into every day experience. Out of this came the

Baye Fall community, a powerful merging of Islamic mysticism with the pragmatism of the African warrior, dedicated to mastery of the self and devotion in action towards others.

On my second day in Senegal, the owner of the guest house took me to my first Baye Fall celebration, where the Baye Falls, singing for days on end, were hand-pounding tonnes of couscous for the children of their schools.

There, on the night of the Epiphany, I met and married my husband Massamba Fall Sy.

The Baye Fall with their black and white dresses,
(at my question: 'Why black and white?' I was answered for receptive and creative, yin and yang!)
All night they sing LA I LA I LLA ALLAH moving as one, counter clockwise,

These vowels are present in the spiritual chants of many traditions.
AA…. opens the hearts, II…..the vision.
All night they are in unison bringing that oneness in the everyday actions.

To be Baye Fall is devotion in action, beyond the self, for the community.

Worriers that master themselves and give all.
All this comes out of two spirits that work as one.
Amadou Bamba always in white Mame Cheik Ibrahim Fall, (the light), always in black.

The Seed of Joy
by Massamba Fall Sy

Millions Gather Yearly for the
Grand Magal in the holy City of Touba
Founded by the Spiritual Voice against Colonialism
Sufi Cheikh Ahmadou Bamba around 1882
Bamba's voice was Alone
After the Failure of the Fierce
African Resistance
Against Assimilation and Exploitation

After meeting him
The ascetic Mama Cheikh Ibrahima Fall "The Light"
Dedicated his life to him
His tireless work
And his pure vision
And around the same time
Founded the Baye Fall Brotherhood

'My Mission is Similar to the Mission
Of the Sun and the Moon,
They Never Stop from the Beginning
Of Creation to This Day
To Work Toward the Creator
Whatever Gives Nausea to the Vulture
And Makes Hyenas Vomit
Make Sure it Comes to Me
I will Transform it to Purity'

Mame Cheikh Ibrahima Fall

Baye Fall is being at one
With all one's energy
Through devotion and action.
Undertaking all work as a prayer.

The Baye Fall

Recognisable by their hair worn as locks

Their colourful patchwork garments
Beauty made out of rags
Prayer beads around their neck
They do not pray five times a day
Neither do they fast once a year
Some consider them an
Evolution of the Ceddo
Warriors in the old Aristocracy of Senegal

They are Sufis
They own nothing
Sometimes beg for their sustenance

They give Everything

'Baye Fall is like a funnel.,
he does not keep the oil'

'Whoever has not yet polished
his heart from all vanities
will never know joy'

Baye Fall sing all night in a circle and
Rotate counter clockwise
The key into the 'other time'

'La ilaha ill Allah Fall'
resonates from the hearts,
vibrations overwhelming time and space

The circle is the journey back to one's self
There is no beginning, no end
There is only One.

Baye Fall is being at one
With all one's energy
Through devotion and action
Undertaking All Work as Prayer.

The Magickal Lantern:
Transcendental Cinema as the Fifth Tool of Occult Ritual

Raymond Salvatore Harmon

llumination is the cornerstone metaphor for the advanced state of human conscious. In any mystical tradition the state of expanded awareness of the human mind is compared to enlightenment. Even the Luciferian tradition of Judean theology contemporizes the angel Samael as the bringer of light or "lucifer."

This comparison between knowledge and light, this parallel that is drawn in all cultural models stands as a testament to the formation of life and its dependence on the sun's light waves as a provider of the necessary energy to support all living existence. Within the framework of occult tradition one finds numerous references to light as knowledge, and it is necessary to consider that light itself plays an important role in the development of the human mind beyond the physical form. The primary text of Kabalistic tradition is the Zohar, or Book of Light. Many of the tenants of Judean mystical understanding originate within this text and it is not the first in the lineage of the tradition of light.

The use of light in ritual has until now been mainly concerned with providing an atmospheric condition for the environment of the ritual. Via various means this theatric tool is often employed to alter the perceived nature of a given environment or experience. The play of shadows, isolation and delivery of light in a cathedral, grove, or ancient temple sets the mood and alters the normal state of the mind.

In considering the delivery of light as medium for illumination one must approach it as scientifically as possible. Isolating causes and effects based on content, environment, staging, sound conditions and overall form. By creating a specific shape to the overall delivery of light to the participant one can achieve the maximum result in reordering the participants perceptual experiences.

The ancient model for light delivery within the framework of initiatory ritual began in the Grecian mysteries of the ancient world. In the west theatrical tools for ritual performance developed over a period from the ancient Mediterranean through the middle-ages on to contemporary religious models like the Catholic mass. Within this framework lighting is a generalized effect, its delivery more closely associated with the staging and sound effects of the environment. But light (or its lack thereof) is in many ways the primary source of the temperament and mood of a given ritual. Even today the practitioner of any spiritual self-exploration uses lighting to set the mood, be it candles, lamps, or more sophisticated lighting effects.

To the mind of the ancient and pre renaissance initiate the theatrical model of ritual performance presented a very distinct and realistic portrayal of specifically chosen story forms from within their religious pantheon. Often in conjunction with some mind-altering substance (alcohol, herbs, etc) the initiate was presented with what appeared to be visions of the mythological representations of their then contemporary deities. In fact a theatrical staging of such events was occurring, providing a backdrop for the initiates passage through the levels of the experience. Although this early theatric model of ritual form has evolved in the past several thousand years, often in conjunction with architectural advances in the presentation of the religious environment, its basic structure is rooted in a theatrical stage play form.

The mind of the modern individual experiencing the 21st century is much more complex and able to handle a much wider and higher resolution area of information than that of its forbearers. The advent of visual effects in film and constant exposure to incoming data from various media has pushed the mind of the average person beyond its ability to be enveloped in the illusion and effect of the staged ritual. Suspension of disbelief is a much harder thing to come by in an advancing information based society.

Cinema as a model of human expression both artistically and scientifically has presented a form with the maximum of integration with the contemporary human mind. Its form – a play of light, illusion of motion, reproductions of sound – gives the filmmaker an expansive palette with which to approach the conscious and subconscious mind of the viewer.

The mind is not only receptive to the illusion that is cinema, but the modern human mind actually works with the principles of cinema (frame rate, cut editing, point of view) to an astounding degree. The human mind often filters out data it deems unnecessary (excessive reverb in a sound environment will be reduced by the mind regardless of the input sound at the ear level; a quick movement of the head will result in the mind visually 'holding' a frame of the last image the eye saw before movement so as not to cause disorientation during the quick movement.) Between the mind's self-editing process and the flicker rate of a cinematic experience we find a tool in the search for a comparative experience for the contemporary initiate.

From its inception cinema has dealt with the illusion of motion and the representation of the fantastical within the ordinary. The first men to present cinema to the public were spiritualists and stage mediums whose utilisation of technological breakthroughs in order to heighten there performances created the original term 'magic lantern.'

But merely representing what seem to be magical, miraculous or illuminating events will not push the contemporary initiate into a state of advanced spiritual awareness. Due to the level of sophistication we have developed in regards to filtering media in our environment we now regard such illusions as HAVING to be created by some technology, for what other means could there be?

So in order to present the initiate with a visual sensory input model that is comparable both to the level and degree of the contemporary mind's abilities we must challenge its actual perceptions of the real. Not by presenting a fictionalised version of the real (as the initiate will simply regard this as illusion and trickery) but by representing the visual field with an evolving abstract pattern of light. One which, due to its lack of representational form, allows the mind to 'project' its own concepts onto the evolving abstractions.

Brion Gysin, contemporary of William Burroughs, created a device that worked within the principles of light as actively used in ritual meditation. The Dream Machine was a very simple device using a record player, sheet of paper with holes and light bulb in order to created projected patterns of evolving light in a room. (The flicker rate of the light dependent on the speed of the turntable and the brightness of the lamp.) Though simple in design the Dream Machine represents the second chain of evolution in the development of the Transcendental Cinema.

Modern video technology represents a much more sophisticated variable for use in the creation of complex abstract patterns than a simple light machine. In a multiple projector environment the illusion of depth can be achieved, and with a very fine degree of control over colour, form, brightness and flicker rate. Once we have approached the mind with a visual input stream beyond the ordinary we can tune this stream to the needs of a given ritual. Colour, flicker rate, form, speed all can be used in order to maximize the minds wave-forms and thought patterns toward a specified ritual goal. When used in conjunction with subliminal content, isotonic audio patterns, and surround sound environments the encompassing transcendental cinematic experience becomes the modern equal to the ancient initiatory mysteries.

Transcendental cinema is the use of film or video to induce a state of the conscious mind beyond that of the ordinary. To create a cinematic experience utilising complex content manipulated in order to achieve specific states of mental awareness. Using the sensory inputs' access to the subconscious mind in order to push the participant away from the sense of self, and toward a sense of the beyond.

+++

Within the realm of mystical traditions (from a contemporary perspective) technology is often shunned. A yearning tends to exist in the average practitioner for a time 'before technology' and a returning to what is perceived as a more pure and straightforward period in humanity's spiritual past.

This perception of the past is illusory. The practitioners of the spiritual methodologies of the past relied on the most complex technologies available to them. From astounding knowledge of psychochemical structures to technological advancements in architecture, language, mathematics, and altered states of the human mind. The priests, shamans, initiates and participants of any spiritual belief system have relied for countless ages on whatever technology had to offer for the presentation and exploration of the spiritual self, whether group or individual.

Aleister Crowley's Rites of Eleusis represented a breakthrough in theatrical forms of improvisation and an advancement of the form of the Greek Mystery into 20th Century avant-garde theatre. Paralleled in Artaud, Gombrowicz, Ionesco, and decades ahead of its time it is now a theatrical form that is a century old.

If the modern magickian or spiritual initiate seeks the farthest path away from the self, and is indeed looking to achieve illumination, the use of all the available knowledge and tools of the contemporary world need to be utilised. Only when we are prepared to travel the furthest away from 'here' will we be able to begin our journey.

+++

Abandonment of the traditional model of ritual theatre is not necessary in order to make use of transcendental cinema within a given working. The two forms, theatric and cinematic, can be brought together to create a set and setting that is ideal for the practice of ritual, in either group or individual workings.

The placement of projected light in an environment should be based on the needs of the participants in the ritual in terms of exposure to that light. Facing into the reflection of projected light from a wall, screen, or other surface will most often allow for the sense of envelopment in a films visual field. When the cinematic light is being 'performed' as part of the ritual it is often best to create a setup that allows for the 'confinement' of the projected light. Allowing the light to be the receptacle for both the projected energies of the participants and the evoked energies of the ritual. Thus the use of transcendental cinema as the Magickal Lantern within the context of the traditional ritual can bring about an astounding spiritual experience. Amplifying the ritual's power and creating an all encompassing setting for the ritual to take place within.

Yet beyond its role within the context of the traditional ritual the use of transcendental cinema as a tool for the expansion and exploration of the human mind in relation to the beyond is in itself independent. Just as cinema no longer has need for the trappings of theatre, the Magickal Lantern of Transcendental Cinema will evolve into its own singular form of experiential ritual archetype. Once it has shed its earlier form it will be more capable of delivering the mind of mankind to the threshold of the beyond, and to open the doors of perception to the light of truth.

Obviam lux Lucis.

Orryelle Defenestrate-Bascule

Sound at Sacred Spaces

Paul Devereux

developing branch of archaeology called 'archaeoacoustics' (the study of sound at archaeological sites) is now beginning to provide the soundtrack to ancient places, in the sense that sound can give us more information about them. Archaeoacoustics is revealing that sound was important to people as far back into time as we can probe – in short, archaeology has discovered that ancient people had ears!

Knocking on rock

The old stones can directly issue sounds. For example, inside the painted caves of France and Spain, which date back tens of thousands of years to the Palaeolithic era, it has been found that some of the stalactites and stalagmites will issue pure bell- or harp-like notes when struck. Close examination has revealed that these calcite features display percussion marks so ancient that they have coverings of calcite deposits.

Other types of rock can also ring or make musical notes. These 'lithophones' or 'rock gongs' are now being identified at many sites. In Africa, two hundred lithophones have been found close to prehistoric rock art panels near the fourth cataract of the Nile, and are also in Nigeria, Tanzania, and other parts of the continent. Nigerian tribesmen can make certain lithophones sound just like their range of tribal drums, which raises the question which came first – percussion on rocks or percussion on drums? In the Americas, ringing rocks have been found at ancient vision quest sites – lonely places to which Indians retreated to fast and go without sleep for days in the hope of receiving a vision. A few years ago in the southern Deccan, India, a Cambridge-Indian archaeological team were studying Stone Age engravings along a rocky ridge when a local man came up and struck the boulders with a small stone: to the archaeologists' astonishment they rang like bells. These rock markings date back 4,000 years, but it is perhaps not coincidental that a not very far away in southern India there are certain temples in which single blocks of rock are able to emit musical sounds – some of them even yielding the seven key notes of classical Indian – music when struck. These features seemingly date to around 700 A.D. – did the Stone Age use of natural ringing rocks develop into a sophisticated art in India?

A research project from the Royal College of Art, involving the present writer, is making a detailed audio-visual study of Mynydd Preseli, southwest Wales, source of the Stonehenge bluestones (the shorter stones at the monument). Some of these spotted dolerite rocks are being found to issue, variously, pure bell-like notes, tin drum sounds, or deep bass gong-like rumbles in the very outcrops from where the Stonehenge stones were extracted. (Follow this project at *www.landscape-perception.com*) It has been a mystery as to why the

Percussionist Z'EV hammers out a rhythm on the musical rocks on Carn Menyn, Preseli, Wales. (Photo: Paul Devereux. Copyright: Landscape & Perception Project)

Preseli bluestones were taken almost two hundred miles to Stonehenge – they clearly had something special about them. Was sound a factor? The clue might be in the name of a Preseli village – Maenclochog (ringing stones or bell rocks).

The spirits speak

Echoes are another type of natural sound associated with some sacred places. A classic example occurs at Mazinaw Rock, a cliff-face rising out of Mazinaw Lake in Ontario. The area is known as Bon Echo Provincial Park because the cliff-face produces remarkable echoes. Along the bottom of the cliff just above the waterline (a conjunction that enhances echoes) are two hundred panels of red ochre paintings produced by ancestral Algonquin people about a thousand years ago. They cluster where the echoes are strongest. This fits in with an Algonquin belief that spirits (manitous) lived inside cliffs and rocks, and that shamans in trance could pass through the rock surface to obtain 'rock medicine' beyond. Indeed, this belief was held by many American Indian peoples and probably other peoples around the world – it is known to have existed in southern Africa, for instance. We moderns take sound for granted in our noisy world, but to

Paul Devereux 'working the night shift' at Carn Menyn, on the Preseli Hills in Wales, source of the Stonehenge bluestones, recording a lithophone.

ancient peoples it could be magical, especially when issuing as music or ghostly echoes from rocks.

There are numerous other ways rocks can make sounds. For instance, Petroglyph Rock, Ontario, is a huge, flattish outcrop of rock covered with ancient engravings. Why that particular rock? Other, similar rock surfaces around are unmarked. It may be because Petroglyph Rock has a deep fissure cutting across it – at times ground water runs along the bottom of the crack causing noises remarkably like whispering voices. Consequently, the rock may well have become the centre for an oracle cult, where answers to questions could be interpreted in the whispering noises being issued form the crack. In Britain, as a different type of example, there is a rock known as the Blowing Stone, near Oxford. When a certain weathered hole is blown into, it issues a sound like the call of an elk or stag. It may have been used in prehistory for animal magic rituals.

Ancient wisdom enters the laboratory

Archaeologists have now also started to use electronic equipment to probe the sonic secrets of ancient monuments. One Anglo-American team, from International Consciousness Research Laboratories (ICRL), Princeton, used instrumentation to test the primary resonance frequencies of Stone Age chambered monuments – that is, the lowest frequency that produced a standing wave within a chamber. They discovered that despite their differing sizes, all the structures they tested resonated in a narrow acoustic frequency band of 95-125 Hertz (cycles per second), with most focusing on 110 Hz.

Subsequent experimental brain research has shown this frequency (the lower baritone range of the human voice) to have a marked and unexpected effect on parts of the brain: in tests with 30 subjects, the lowest activity area in the right frontal lobe of the brain switched over completely to the left frontal lobe, while the temporal cortex (at either side of the brain, and associated with language processing) also quietened, though less dramatically so. This regional effect on brain activity was at its maximum at precisely 110 Hz, just as if a switch was thrown. The subjective implications of this are currently not understood, but the effect only occurs in the brain's theta range of electrical activity, which is usually associated with trance and associated conditions. But much more investigation is required to properly explore these findings. (For the scientific paper on this, see I. Cook, et al., 'Ancient Architectural

Acoustic Resonance Patterns and Regional Brain Activity', *Time & Mind*, March 2008)

Archaeological acoustic research is in its infancy as yet but it is already providing new insights about ancient places and will surely allow the old stones to tell us more of their secrets in the years to come.

One of the larger sections of the fallen and broken Er Grah standing stone, Brittany, France. Thought to have been the largest megalith ever erected, it is a lithophone – it rings when struck. (Photo: Paul Devereux)

Meditation-stele 22 - Fredrik Söderberg

It's music that you make, it's magic that you hear.

Mark Pilkington

magic is music is magic is music is magic is magic is music is magic is music is magic is

pen your ears and the whole world is music.

The whisper of a breeze through trees; the hum of a refrigerator; the crunch of dry earth underfoot; the clatter of waves on a pebble beach.

This act of listening, of transformation, of interpretation, of imagination, of forging a relationship between the self and the universe beyond, is also the essence of magic.

Or at least one form of it. Here are some more variants, their boundaries necessarily blurred.

It might be music of action and raw power. It might be music of transcendence and otherworld journey, into the vastness of Outer Space or the luminous darkness of Inner Space. It might be music created to be magical action, or music created during magical action. It might be music of form, sound revealed for what it is – physical vibration acting upon space and matter. It might be music of place, site specific actions imbued with the genius loci or genius temporis. It might be music of rebellion and defiance, drawing on cultural opposition and taboo for its power. It might be music of unity, a powerful experience shared by all those at a gig or club.

Or it might just be you, listening quietly.

Music and magic are twins. They were born together and will never part.

Music and song are central to the lives of almost all animal species and we humans are no different. Archaeologist Steven Mithen has suggested that our Neanderthal cousins, who lived in Europe between about 200,000 and 35,000 years ago, communicated in high-pitched sing-song voices, and that words and language evolved from these musical sounds. Did a similar evolutionary process take place in our own species? Perhaps humans and Neanderthals sang together in interspecies harmony, at least when they weren't eating each other. Today humans and birds sing together, while elephants and bonobos in captivity are learning to play human instruments. Song communicates across species boundaries; and we can imagine this as one of the earliest forms of magic.

Music can not have been far behind song. An alleged 43,000 year old bone 'flute' – two holes punched into the femur of a cave bear found at Divje Babe, a Neanderthal settlement in Slovenia – remains controversial; but a number of bone flutes found in China, many still playable, have been dated to 9,000 years ago. To put this into perspective, 9000 years ago humans were beginning to settle down into distinct cultures, developing agriculture and animal husbandry. The great pyramids of Egypt and the grandest stone circles of Northern Europe were still 4500 years into the future, and we are another 4500 years ahead of them. What will our descendants be listening to in 4500 years time?

Magic and music gave rise to all human culture. In hunter-gatherer societies, music and dance mimicked (and still do) the cries and movements of prey animals, and animal calls were made during the hunt. These rites evolved into more complex performances with multi-layered meanings – the first theatres of magic. Shamans employed song and dance, often along with hallucinogenic extracts from plants or animals, to heal and to harm, and to mediate between our world and that of nature's other creations, between the physical world and the world of spirit.

Those cultures that experienced dramatic expansion saw some of their shamans become priests and the music stayed with them, and remains with us today. Chanting is a powerful transcendental tool whether you are Buddhist, Christian, Hindu, Jew or Muslim; ecstatic drumming and dance still dictate the pace of the African-root religions – Candomblé, Obeah, Santeria, Voodoo.

That old magic is still with us, permeating our culture, flowing a course through time. It is everywhere, fragmenting and evolving with every new generation. And it is up to us to tap into it. Some of us will find magic by ourselves. Some of us prefer the structure of groups and organisations. Some of us don't yet realise that we've found it.

In our days there are as many styles, colours and definitions of magic as there of music. As in music you will find traditional approaches or genres – wiccan, heathen, voodoo, hoodoo, thelemite, luciferian – and fractionalisations of each. Find the route that takes you there, but the first lessons of magic are to be aware and to be awake. Knowledge is power. Much of the assumed power of organised magical structures resides in notions of tradition – of secret wisdom passed down through countless ages. However, in the Western world at least, most esoteric traditions began as fantasies of tradition; many aren't much older than the blues. Most contemporary practitioners are aware of this and have no problem with it, others have generated new traditions that speak to them more profoundly than off-the-peg systems. First find the magic, then shape it to your own needs. And music is as good a place as any to start looking.

If it's transcendence and real tradition that you want, you can find it in music. By beating a drum or plucking a string, you are engaging with systems and states of mind that stretch back centuries, even millennia. And your tools don't have to be ancient. Electricity is one of the supreme manifestations of natural magic, while the qabalistic paths and flowing sigils of synthesiser waveforms – my own tools of choice – are about the same age as wicca.

So, choose your instrument, find your magic, use your imagination and remember...

music is magic is music is magic is magic is music is magic is music is magic is music is

An altered version of this piece appeared in the 2008 Supersonic Festival programme.

Witch God by Edwin Pouncey

Black Mountain
Matthew Wiley

I have traveled through
the labyrinth to face the Bull.

Bouncing off the bodies
of my brothers and sisters
upon the Black Mountain.
If only momentarily,
I shed reserve.

The teaching of the Secret Snake.

I have wept with the Goddess,
and turned to face the Mysteries as I am.

Naked in the All Knowing -
bare before the still point
.
I have bound and untied
the Knot of Secrets, and
flung myself back home.

I have climbed the craggy slope,
alone in Omens

I have been taught
by bird and tree.

I have looked. I have seen.

Upon the bridge of becoming I faced
the horrors of my being -there I was
mocked with Love, and a
new Freedom took root.

I have Drummed and Danced.

I partook of sacred flesh and dissolved
constraints of hardened pattern in
the womb of Earth and Wood.

I have defiled my robes and
put them on fresh again.

115

Oh Goddess Whore and Virgin,
I have held your hands.

My tears fall forth and
spill from your eyes.

In love I followed you
into the Secret Mountain....
In search I followed you into
the Secret Mountain..

In hope of Restoration and Balance
you led me into the Black Mountain.

CONVERSATIONS

Thoughts on the Winter Bloom
Comus
An interview with the reawakened

Raymond Salvatore Harmon

It has become almost commonplace for bands once thought lost to reunite for a tour, a gig for a good cause or sometimes more rarely to record new material. Yet the reawakening of Comus is something that no one ever imagined could happen.

Based in Bromley, Kent, the band recorded two obscure records in the 1970s (1971's *First Utterance* and the followup record for Virgin in 1974 *To Keep from Crying*) and then quietly faded into obscurity. Over the ensuing years legions of folk freaks from all backgrounds have stumbled on the seminal First Utterance and been consumed by the power of its range, its subtle dark shadows and the passion of its madness.

While the roots of its influence have extended far and wide and its members have lived their lives, Comus has slept. And now it has awakened, its songs returning to quicken the heart and enflame the soul once more.

We took the opportunity to ask some relevant questions to the band, in the hopes of shedding light on the missing pages from Comus' history.

+++

Comus' music contains themes of strong primordial urges and dark imagery. What inspired this material at a time when most folk music was dominantly centered on light and festivity?

Bobby Watson (vocals, percussion): 'I think that the subject matter came from Roger's imagination as a young man. At the time he had an interest in the outer reaches of society, subcultures, death, sex, – extremes generally.'

Glenn Goring (guitar): 'It's difficult to pinpoint our motives/sources from such a distance in time but I remember when Roger and I first started playing in traditional folk clubs, we'd follow act after act regurgitating the same old songs and I personally had a strong sense that something needed shaking up. There was such a formal, stodgy, almost resigned atmosphere about these places. It was as if the audience and the performers had turned into zombies. When we started crashing out Velvet Underground numbers – 'shiny boots of leather' etc – on two beaten-up instruments they didn't know where to look. It was like musical vandalism. Roger and I blew away their cobwebs and they didn't like it. I guess that same principle applied as we went on to form the fully-fledged Comus. But having said all that have heard some fantastic traditional folk singers over the years. I don't want to come across as knocking the genre in its entirety. This was my experience at the time.'

119

Roger Wootton (guitar, lead vocals): 'I have been asked these questions many times. I think what galvanised me in the first place was a combination of reacting against a cruel and repressive middle class back ground and a disillusionment with the hippie movement. The love and peace doctrine soon disintegrated into 'all property is theft. What's yours is everyone else's but what's mine's my own' and the ethos of 'Turn on, tune in, drop out', was futile because you won't change anything by dropping out – it should have been 'drop in' – and the passivity and liberalism led to chaos and lack of initiative. I had had a rural background and that influence and the republication of *The Lord of the Rings* had a major impact (plus a good deal of drug experimentation). Other than that it is hard to precisely latch on to what drew me in that primal direction. It was very instinctual rather than intellectually preconceived.'

Regarding the band's formation, it was a gradual development and the combined chemistry which emerged around my writing. It was luck really. Just chance that the right people fell together and formulated the sound and energy, although there were a few line up changes before we formed the six on First Utterance.'

Obviously there has been a bit of downtime between the last record of Comus and the recent revival. What caused this sudden reawakening?

Bobby: 'The reissue of the Comus material in 2005, and hence the interest by Stefan Dimle, (Melloboat Festival organiser) and Mikael Ackerfeldt of Opeth. Then of course the first performance in 35 years at the Melloboat Festival in March 2008.'

Glenn: 'It all started with Sanctuary's re-release of the Comus 'back catalogue' *Song to Comus* in 2005. A reunion soon followed which kind of broke the ice for what was to come. Some months went by and a guy at Sanctuary forwarded me an email from a Swedish fan called Stefan Dimle asking if Comus would play on his floating festival the Melloboat in March 2008. I replied to the man at Sanctuary that Stefan had more chance of seeing God than Comus reforming (God might still turn up)! There were lots of grumblings and mumblings between us about whether to just make an appearance at the 'party' as Stefan called it. But then certain members got their teeth into the idea of actually reforming and slowly, painfully the beast staggered back to life.'

(120)

Roger: 'We were asked if we were interested in reforming from about 2002 onwards. In 2005 Sanctuary offered us a record deal, but we all agreed at the time that there was too much water under the bridge and none of us wanted to commit. Finally in 2007, Mikael Åckerfeldt and Stefan Dimle encouraged us and offered us the Melloboat Festival in Stockholm. We really capitulated as a result of pressure to reform. The steady build up through file sharing has brought us to the attention of a new and much younger audience, who don't mind how old we are. They just love the music. We have this advantage that the music is so original it doesn't sound dated. It took some time to relate back to the Comus feel and at first it almost felt like a tribute band learning someone else's material. Then came writing new songs. We agreed that we had to psych back into post *First Utterance* mode and before Malgaard to make the album that should have been but never was – *Second Utterance*, so to speak – with songs that followed on from *First Utterance*. The

∞

first has been completed, appropriately titled 'Out of the Coma'. We have been asked to perform the whole of *First Utterance* at the Equinox Festival and we shall be performing 'Out of the Coma' for the encore. More material is on the way.'

In the meantime between the last record and now Comus has grown into an almost mythic group. Projects like the rumored concept album Malgaard Suite, *have become legendary via chat room speculation. Over the years were the members of the band aware of the cult-like status of Comus?*

Bobby: 'I wasn't in the least! It came as a total shock and disbelief when I saw the reviews on the Progarchives website! I thought that we were totally lost in oblivion, and that someone was having a joke with me! When I saw the comments coming from fans on our Myspace site, it all started to become real – these were just normal people who were obviously genuine in their huge fanship of Comus.'

Glenn: 'As the Internet grew so did interest in the band and it's obviously down to mass communication – blogs, downloads, chat rooms etc – that Comus have generated such a following, which is just amazing. Over the years, long before the band re-united, I could see more and more information appearing about Comus, mainly in reference to *First Utterance*, and most of it was very positive, bordering on the adulatory. Sometimes (often in disbelief) I had to read the reviews several times before the content sank in. It was a very entertaining phenomenon to follow from a distance, so to speak. But for you to mention the word 'mythic' though really is astonishing. I can understand the 'cult' label and I think that evolved merely because nothing was known about us, who we were, what we were doing, etc but 'mythic'? I have to say that a lot of my friends and acquaintances were not even aware, until quite recently, that I ever played in an acid folk band, let alone Comus.

121

However, over the years I have performed intermittently. In the eighties, I was in a band called the Hollow Men and since then I've played a kind of Flamenco/jazz/folk hybrid as part of a duo. You mentioned the Malgaard suite, well, I remember it as a bit of a curate's egg. It was about twenty minutes long and quite convoluted, lots of passages of alternating moods and rhythms. It had an epic quality that, like most Comus music, didn't fit comfortably into a single genre. I think it was still evolving as a piece even though we were performing it live. We played it at several venues and the audience's bemusement was tangible.'

There seems an almost lycanthropic or animistic element to Comus. Much like its namesake the music seems constantly on the verge of losing control. Such an inspired Dionysian sense of urgency in the music is amplified by the fact that so little is known about the performers. Are their any revealing events in the lives of the members that would account for such a powerful range of emotions?

Bobby: 'I wouldn't say so. I think that it is simply the result of Roger's powerful imagination, and that he was a bit of a loner. Speaking personally, I can only say that I have always been passionate about music generally, and that anything that I've been involved in, I have always given all my commitment – if I do something I do it seriously. There were no specific events in my life, apart from being a horrendously rebellious teenager!'

Glenn: 'Nothing specific that I can think of, but the group dynamic is more or less what it always was. We're all quite highly strung and being together is a bit like being in the company of someone wearing an impish grin while juggling hand grenades.'

Thirty years later the music still holds an incredible amount of power. Taking the stage again as a collective to do this material after so many years reveals how amazing this material and the group that created it are – any thoughts on the winter bloom that Comus is now enjoying?

Bobby: 'Yes, well, I think that you've named the primary thing – the quality of the material. I could never have been enthusiastic about it if I didn't think it was worth spending time and energy on reviving. I knew it was good stuff, and that's why I committed myself to it, despite the fact that the type of material Jon Seagroatt and I had been working on with our other bands was totally different to say the least! The material is also unlike any other band's. I have always been concerned in any creative work I do, that I'm not involved with anything run of the mill or predictable. I always wanted to be different.

Of course it's great to be admired and wanted, and I am doing my best to give our fans some of what they want (i.e. performances), and to take advantage of opportunities that come our way. Not many people of our ages get this sort of second chance.

We are planning a US tour for early next year, (the planned one this year had to be cancelled due to unforeseen visa problems), and new material is being written. We hope to play more dates in this country. It's hard to progress as fast as we'd like to, as running Comus could easily be a full time job!

I think it's incredibly exciting, and we are so lucky to have such a fanatical, devoted fanbase. This kind of thing happening is not what anybody could ever have imagined. We are trying to grasp it firmly with both hands!'

Glenn: 'I have to pinch myself, really. I'm quite a reclusive person so I've had to do a bit of readjustment to emerge into this new and very public daylight. I'm still somewhat ambivalent about the exposure. Yet, at the same time, I find it all very compelling and the best thing is being in the midst of the 'noise' again. I forgot how dramatic the music sounds. And what a dedicated performer Roger is.

123

The gig on the Melloboat was a pretty scary occasion, we had absolutely no idea whatsoever how our music was going to be received. When Roger struck-up the first notes of 'Song to Comus' there was this incredible roar from the audience – it was like 35 years of bottled emotion being released. I was so shocked by the reaction I simply couldn't play for a couple of bars. We were all stunned. I was also amazed to discover that so many fans had come all the way from the US, Japan, and Europe to see us. It was a weird and wonderful moment. It will be very interesting to see what the Equinox Festival audience will make of it.'

The Beauty in not Knowing
An Interview with Æthenor

Andrew Hartwell

'Brooding, primeval, dark alchemical epics are full of a ferocious intensity, sounding more like a starlit night being ripped open by lightning than a musical group. Intelligent and primal, like a dæmonic workshop, battering up Pandemoniums and dreaming of gold and murder, Æthenor are spectacular.' David Tibet

Æthenor are a most atypical musical experience. Combining the talents of Stephen O'Malley (Sunn O))), KTL, Ginnungagap), Daniel O'Sullivan (Guapo, Mothlite, Miasma & The Carousel of Headless Horses) and Vincent De Roguin (Shora) at its core, Aethenor transcend any easy categorisation, their output an ever evolving sum of free, drone, and experimental musics and beyond. The band first came to prominence with their 2006 album *Deep in Ocean Sunk the Lamp of Light* (VHF records), a sumptuous feast of dark churning drones, metallic scrapes and percussion, heaving organ and aetherial interferences. Housed in a beautiful hand-screened natural board package, this set a high benchmark for all following works both musically and aesthetically. The following *Betimes Black Cloudmasses* (VHF, 2008) saw the project evolve yet further with the notable additions of free percussionists Nicolas Field and Alex Babel, increasing the focus and intensity of the sound as the group conjured a new and miasmic psychedelia. The appearance of Ulver's Kristoffer Rygg on the album, contributing vocals and effects, only intensified the sense of purpose and confirmed the tag of 'supergroup'.

While European audiences were able to bask in the band's live performances, few could imagine that things would take a further 'kvlt' turn. *Faking Gold and Murder* added yet more grist to the mill in the shape of David Tibet (Current 93), who contributed lyrics and vocals. Further guitar and vocal work was provided by Alexander Tucker, noted for his excellent avant folk recordings and stunning live performances. This is perhaps on of the most remarkable facets of Æthenor: the ability of so many stellar musicians and visionary creators to be able to come together in such a way, where individual performances blend so seamlessly in the creation of a of new and unexpected vistas.

124

We took the opportunity of quizzing Stephen O'Malley (guitars) and Daniel O'Sullivan (keyboards) prior to their Equinox appearance.

How did Aethenor come about? As none of you have ever lived in the same country at any stage (as far as I am aware) it seems like an unlikely project to come to fruition. Was recording always intended to take place together, in the same physical space, or was it conceived as a project whereby you would all work on parts and submit them via the Internet or by some similar method?

Daniel O'Sullivan: 'I met Stephen years ago at the first Sunn O))) performance in London. In one guise or another, we've been collaborating ever since. Vincent and I met in Geneva; he was involved in booking a Guapo show there. We put down some overnight improvisations to embellish on some recordings he and Stephen had made together. It was initially more of an audio collage and the sessions for the *Deep in Ocean...* album were particularly segregated whereas the *Betimes* and *Faking Gold* recordings were conceived and arranged way in advance. We played all night in a disused meat locker in Geneva, both myself and Vincent and two percussionists, Alex Babel and Nicolas Field. We then spent two years on and off editing and overdubbing with Stephen, Antti Uusimaki, Kris Rygg, David Tibet, and Alexander Tucker. We actually stumbled upon a sound quite accidentally on *Deep in Ocean* that we wilfully elaborated on with the proceeding albums. Since then it has become more of solid live entity involving myself, Vincent, Stephen, Kris and Steve Noble, one of the most innovative and breathtaking drummers I have had the pleasure of working with.'

Did you intend to perform live from the outset? Did you know in advance what direction the music would take?

Daniel: 'The beauty of Æthenor is not knowing. It's somewhat of a relief compared to the other work we're all involved in. Of course there were some initial ideas that we considered using as catalysts, it might be a mode, a scale, or even just a gesture, but the pruning of those ideas are entirely automatic and the real gold is often when we go 'off-route'.'

You all come from well-known bands which are already at the fringes of the avant garde. Would you agree that Aethenor has set the destination as 'Further'? Where are you aiming to get to?

Daniel: 'The goalposts shift a lot of the time, due to the amorphous nature of the music. One thing we can all rely on is our intuition as musicians, I think we've grown to have a lot of faith in each other's facility and execution. When you have that trust, the destination is simply pleasure. Of course, pleasure can be conceived in quite a contrary way in terms of the audience's perspective. '

Stephen O'Malley: 'In my opinion it's not the destination, and it's a more traditional approach. Probably something closer to jazz and experimental music of the early '90s, but something more unified musically. At least with regards to the live band, which I am involved in, I can't speak for the production of the albums as I have generally not been involved in that process beside a few tracking sessions. To me Æthenor actually is trying to operate in a conceptually looser, musically less strict manner. There's a lot of illusionary references and text thrown around but in fact the music is almost entirely improvised with very little musical theory involved. This may develop as or if the live setting continues but that's a development of band chemistry and personality.
    This said, it's enjoyable on a level that approaches ecstasy at the best live and living moments of the music.'

How did the connection with VHF come about? The packaging is always remarkable in its execution: who comes up with the visual identity for each record?

Daniel: 'From the very beginning, it was decided that one of Vincent's roles was to design the album covers, as another outlet of his artistic contribution to Æthenor. This can sometimes be a bone of contention as we are all visually oriented people, but the results always outweigh the tension.'

Stephen: 'VHF does a great great job with the detail and production of the Æthenor records. I've had a good contact with Bill Kellum at VHF for several years mainly through my interest in Jack Rose and Pelt. We loosely talked about working together and when the first Æthenor record was prepared I proposed the label to the others as an option and it worked. Vincent de Roguin is very strict about his direction and control with executing the design and aesthetic of the records, and the results speak for themselves.'

Would you say there is an 'occult agenda' to Æthenor? Are the ideas behind each album part of a whole or does each record exist in its own world? Deep in Ocean sunk the Lamp of Light *is a quotation from Homer, if I am not mistaken. What are the origins for the other album titles? Do the titles act as a guide for the group, as an idea along which to channel certain feelings and tones to the music? Who guides that process?*

Daniel: 'I answered a similar question recently with regard to the use of symbolism in Miasma & the Carousel of Headless Horses. There was always a great empathy for spiritualism in my family. There were constant stories of the paranormal, séances, hauntings, etc. Of course what ensued was a teenage fascination with occult literature. John Dee, Crowley, Lautreamont and then later on to more fruitful esoteric pursuits with Mircea Eliade, Rene Guenon, Carl Jung, Joscelyn Godwin, etc. To be honest my interest in that area transgressed from a naive flirtation to something much more practical and meaningful. That 'occult agenda' as you put it is no longer a main concern for me. For sure, there are a lot of occult references within Æthenor. The very name is an amalgam of Greco-Latin and 16th Century alchemical terminology, but these notions are conduits to explaining the real occult sensibility in the band that has more to do with our individual biorhythms and responses to each other and the sounds we create, and that feeling of ecstatic weightlessness that we touch on from time to time. Transcendence.'

You have worked with some pretty phenomenal guests, such as David Tibet and Kris Rygg. How did these collaborations come about? Do you have more collaborations planned?

127

Stephen: 'Again, these were long-term connections I have had, and the time seems right. The phenomena of collaboration can be an exciting and outstanding one and I think that both of these crossings prove that.'

Daniel: 'Actually, Kris and I met over Myspace. I wrote him a note about how impressed as I was by the *Blood Inside* record, he responded with equally appreciative words on the Miasma album, *Perils*. Since then we've become dear friends and we collaborate with each other whenever there is an opportunity to do so. Kris' contributions to Æthenor have led to my involvement with the live incarnation of Ulver, which is very exciting indeed.'

How do you feel about the Equinox festival: do you think it's valid to try and combine 'organised' occultism with more occult 'informed' arts such as experimental film and music? We don't think anyone has ever really attempted a festival on this scale before that unifies diverse strands of occult/spiritual practice under one banner.

Daniel: 'Absolutely. I think it's integral for these ideas to be expressed through multifarious disciplines. Gurdjieff's concept of the Fourth Way, for example, was made all the more potent through the medium of his sacred dances and harmonium improvisations. Art and theory inform each other constantly and in many ways, the filmmakers and musicians that you're talking about are exemplifying ideas put forward by a more scholastic occultism. However, my personal lifestyle choices are not dictated by any particular regulation. In fact, I am a complete contradiction of most occult-oriented texts I've had the persistence to read. I have a predilection towards life and love. Love being… the law.'

Stephen: 'I have little to do with 'organised' occultism or religion, it simply doesn't inform my way of living. I do have a huge interest in psychology, shamanism, philosophy and alternate, flexible worldviews, topics that occult topics seems to satisfy at times. I believe strongly that the process of creating music and artwork can be defined as a 'magical', 'transcendent', 'communal', 'evocative' or 'alchemical' one, if you want to operate in the lingo of the occult. I personally get excited by intensely energetic and spiritually charged music and artwork, this is my angle… any implied requirement of validation or conviction within some system is irrelevant if that energy is there. The energy is the life and most crucial evidence.'

Does any occult/spiritual practice inform your daily lives? Do you think that music is/can be an expression of occult practice? Whenever I think about this it seems there's two usual strands – Black Metal and Industrial (dark ambient or whatever you want to call it): undoubtedly there are some bands and individuals within these scenes who are genuine, though I feel many of them rely on school yard bravado and outward appearance. Do you think overt outward manifestation can ever be entirely removed from being merely marketing?

Stephen: 'I addressed this partially in my last answer. Music and art are shrouded in marketing in accordance to its commodification, that's the name of the game. Whether or not something is or isn't honest or realistically delivered I think becomes completely obvious to one who is also aware and able to approach honestly and without influence of that prior mentioned shroud. But some people like to play with these things because 1) they are cool topics or images or 2) they are tricksters (sometimes misinterpreted as posing), 3) they are looking for an accepted aesthetic and community where for their particular vision should lie, or 4) they are explorers. I think its interesting to play with all of these elements (as we have done with Sunn O))) in particular) as aesthetics, especially when the fundamental core of the music or art itself is strong enough to actually inspire some sort of spiritual reaching in its audience. And to go beyond any aesthetic and exist on its own terms in its own space of being.

I also think that its crucial to strive to challenge and break the sacred qualities which arise when one's ideas become too comfortable or stable, crystallised. And by challenging these aspect in others, often with venomous reactions, one can continually crack open the possibilities for new development.

To put it bluntly I've met so called scholars in the music world who claim omniscience of all things in one particular topic (jazz, politics, AOS or OTO, or Crowley or Qlippoth or whatever) but who have no clue how to get the stain out of their shirt, tie their shoes, get a girlfriend or offer up any fresh ideas of their own. But I've met the most intense inspiring shamanistic artists who live in the woods (or the middle of Berlin) by themselves with absolutely no desire to prove themselves and work in a produce market for $5 an hour. Bottom line is that painting psychology with 'occult' colours and references may hide the basic psychological principles, but at the end of the day they are just that: basic psychological principles in different colours.'

Lords of Flies:
Barry William Hale's Noko
Jack Sargeant

n a crawlspace below a suburban house, two men have been carving a noise both derived from and contributing to a series of ritual workings that represents over two decades of musical engagement. The air is thick with smoke from tobacco and incense; dim lights fail to illuminate the entire space though a puddle of dirty brown water is visible at the edge of the room. In one corner of the basement a circle is meticulously chalked on the ground; invocations and sigils transverse it, written in careful detail. Candles burn. A handful of chairs and cushions enable the artists and their guests to sit and listen via the intricately wired mixing desk. The sound emerges in a series of fluctuating drones, hums, tweets, mutterings, guttural voices and staggered, endlessly mutable tones. This is Noko's rehearsal and recording space, where experiments are instigated and ideas explored. It is a space of possibility.

Noko started working together in 1993, originally collaborating on the 'Enochian Watchtower' operation. The trio met at art college, although the details of their first meeting are vague. Barry William Hale recalls 'seeing cabbalistic graffiti at the college and seeking out the author' while Scott Barnes and Michael Strum 'had been exploring some free-form audio-visual collaboration'. Following 'the exchange of some documents, including Crowley's Atlantis and the Vision and the Voice', the group commenced an inaugural work based on the 'rigorous investigation of the Great Elemental Watchtowers of the Enochian magical system.'

Noko established a creative practice that Hale and Barnes have rigorously adhered to, with sessions that last between four and eight hours. From such disciplined practice they record between 60 and 90 minutes of audio documentation, which is subsequently edited. Crucially these sounds are not simply viewed as music but are constructed as 'sonotrophic talismans'. The essential part of each recording is improvised, but, over the 16 years of experimentation, systems have developed and an internal consistency has emerged. Throughout the group's history other artists, including Daniel Winter and Michelle Moo, have collaborated with Noko on various projects, and each has brought their own ideas to the group, complimenting and adding to Noko's aesthetic.

Scott Barnes suggests that Noko's aesthetic draws from a broad spectrum of musical genres, having emerged through a process of experimentation and deliberation:

'There is no prescription regarding sonic palette. Noko is primarily constructed in the digital domain, with Barry's voice the obvious live and sampled acoustic source. I often create virtual machines, defining potential phase spaces that generate a variety of outputs. Data mining of these outputs yields raw material, which is then fed back into the compositional process. One aesthetic feature of the Noko sound is the plasticity of various sonic elements, for example a single vocal sample is often transformed into a variety of other textures and rhythms within a piece. Alternately themes may coalesce from disparate fragments or disintegrate into a range of new materials.'

Existing in a kind of permanent twilight, producing work largely for personal satisfaction or to small invited audiences, Noko rarely perform live. Their few releases have been issued in strictly limited numbers. Their last performance, entitled *PA Gsq*, occurred in 2006, in the earthy confines of a former industrial space below a railway bridge in Sydney. It was designed to celebrate the publication of the Australian O.T.O.'s *Waratah III*, and used sound and visuals as a celebratory ritual actualisation.

The period of time between each performance is explained by the group as the result of an extended production period during which every possibility is examined, worked through and engaged with, before being utilised or discarded according to the rigours demanded by the piece. The Equinox Festival will see the premiere of Noko's latest work *Order 41*.

'*Noko Order 41 – The Conjuration of Beelzebub*, is our most detailed construction to date. Pre-production alone has taken around eight months. The work is informed by, and has evolved in parallel to, the publication of *Legion 49* by Barry Hale. This work differs in both its choice of sources and breadth of research. The work is articulated in a

131

sevenfold structure which takes the participant to the arcane deserts of the Middle East, into Plato's Cave and through the inverted spire of the infernal chapel, opening the Gates of Hell, conjuring the Lord of the Flies and his legions. In terms of musicology the work locates and maps loci of Luciferian eruptions into popular culture, sampling and working with sources appropriate to these periods; from medieval pacts and grimoires through to the devil beat of early jazz and seventies Satanic rock, departing with the prophetic first emanations of the *Order 41.*'

The sonic construction augments the accompanying performance and ritual developed by Hale following years of meticulous study. Hale's occult work is inseparable from notions of aesthetic practice in fine art and in sonic art. 'The ritual intention lead us to rigorous integration of relevant materials, tabled by each member in a "Chinese parliament" format.' The materials can include ritual technologies as well as historical precedents, elements of performance, sonic choices and, perhaps crucially, elements of chance.

Part of the strength of Noko's work is the creative relationship between those involved in any project. As Barnes states it emerges from 'the intersection of two or [sometimes] more creative practices.... The ritual has primacy to which the other elements respond.' While working on the piece, magical ritual plays a key aspect.

Noko Order 41 – *The Conjuration of Beelzebub*

'The performances of the rituals are consciousness-altering, which creates feedback loops into the process and effects ongoing aesthetic outcomes. The intersection of the disparate creative practices in the current line-up serves to delineate the space of psychic manifestation and eruption. Burroughs and Gysin described this emergent property as the 'Third Mind', which is appropriate to the description of any group creative dynamic. This, the egregor, is the collective unconscious of the group, defining not only the real time interaction of the elements within a specific working, but the accretion of the whole work history of Noko.'

Notably, while Hale is an initiate, Barnes is not, enabling the creative practice to flow from antithetical approaches to psychological or spiritual development. For Hale his initiation is a manifestation, 'an outward hieroglyph and an inward attainment'. In contrast Barnes is less interested in initiatory structure, seeing his function in Noko as a technician able to help in the realisation of the projects as well as able to engage with the philosophical part of the creative process: 'My role in Noko is a technical one. I am tending the sonic hearth like a church organist. I am also an input regarding philosophical considerations, and see the creative process as very linked to fundamentals of Thelemic discourse, crediting Crowley and other occult luminaries as early adopters of postmodern ideas regarding art practice and consciousness. Of course I have also been subjected to a range of esoteric radiations relating to the ongoing work.'

The creative process is an ongoing experimentation. While various traditions prescribe specific sonic traits for particular ritual purposes, Barnes' sonic vocabulary escapes such attribution. 'Sometimes numeric or gematric information is encoded, but the sonic response to the ritual is intuitive and improvisational. In a broader sense, I am the filter responsible for the sonic palette, making choices appropriate to context that are specific to my own sound practice and the NOKO project. These tonal responses arise in real time as part of the evolving structure of the specific work rather than from a predetermined playbook.'

For the Equinox Festival, Noko anticipate the piece will function as an aural and sonic grimoire, with the ritual unfolding as a performance. Accompanying the performance will be live and archival video by Michael Strum, with images drawn from the unconscious and pulled into the performative context.

EQUINOX FESTIVAL 2009 Timeline Map

TIME	Friday (June 12)		Saturday (June 13)	
	LECTURE	FILM	LECTURE	FILM
	Lecture Room	Main Hall	Main Hall	Brockway Room
11 am	Aaron Gach	The Seed of Joy & American Magus	Robert Wallis	Mock Up on MU
12 pm	Matt Wiley		Philip Farber	
	Masamba Fall		Robert Ansell	
1 pm	Paola Igliori		Paul Devereux	Le Bete & Divine Horsemen
2 pm	Barry Hale's NOKO		Raymond Salvatore Harmon + Rob Mazurek	
3 pm	Kendall Geers	The Holy Mountain	David Beth	Heaven & Earth Magic
4 pm			Erik Davis	
5 pm	DINNER BREAK			
6 pm	MUSIC PERFORMANCES			
7 pm	AT CAMDEN CENTRE		Doors open- In Main Hall	
8 pm	James Ferraro		K11 / Pietro Riparbelli	
	HATI		Yan-gant-y-tan	
			Burial Hex	
9 pm	Z'EV		Kinit Her	
10 pm	John Zorn		Comus	
11 pm				
12 am	Afterparty (at Camden Centre)		Afterparty (venue TBA)	

Notes:
- Friday June 12 evening performances take place at Camden Centre.
- Band stage times subject to change.
- Evening keynote lectures (Erik Davis and Ralph Metzner) take place in the Conway main hall.

Sunday (June 14)	
LECTURE	FILM
Brockway Room	Main Hall
Orryelle Defenestrate-Bascule	Mindscape of Alan Moore
Stephen Grasso	YHVH & The Philosopher's Stone
Marco Pasi	
Edwin Pouncey	Diminishing Shrine Recycles
Arktau Eos	
Carl Abrahamsonn	Leary 8 Circuit & Kings with Straw Mats
Ralph Metzger	
Doors open- In Main Hall	
Chaos Majik	
Pestrepeller	
Dieter Muh	
TAGC	
Æthenor	
Threshold House Boys Choir	
Afterparty (venue TBA)	

- Afterparty locations will be announced at the Festival reception desk at Conway Hall.
- Ritual performances are closed events. No entry once the performance has begun.

FESTIVAL PROGRAMME

Contemporary spiritual exploration
& Mystical Tradtion

136   In presenting the works of the various components of the festival the thought was always to outline a form. A shape that, while composed of individuals with unique ideas and experiences, could cohesively hold together as a totality.

The ideas represented at the Equinox Festival outline various approaches to and commentaries on that which is generally referred to as the 'beyond'. The 'beyond' state is called as many things as there are cultures (gnosis, samadhi, nirvana, satori, etc). What unifies this concept of the beyond, regardless of the label given to it by a particular culture, is the distinct representation of experiential awareness outside of the mundane. Not within or without the self, but beyond.

Man has attempted to achieve and to understand this state for as long as there has been language. Religions have come and gone, ideas have changed and grown, and man still searches for that understanding. That knowing that is ultimately the philosophers stone.

The systems of design that lead one toward this state are countless. Within every cultural model exist multiple paths toward this state, some contradictory, all valid. What remains is that this state, this knowing, is both achievable and understandable. That mankind has gone and returned. That the Journey can still come for anyone attempting to step onto the path.

In contemporary society the information age has changed the very fabric of how we get from moment to moment. This change has altered the way in which man is growing intellectually and spiritually. Access to ideas, philosophies and the practical tools to lead one toward a path of knowing have become easily available to anyone with the desire to look for them.

Many have gone on the path already. Some have brought back practical lessons for the potential journeyer. Others have brought back gifts from the fountain of inspiration that these personal experiences have given to them as artists. In the end these individuals offer us a practical and theoretical approach (and there are many) to finding one's own path toward the light.

In three days a congress of composers, performers, speakers, and cinematic documents will cover a vast range of personal, historical and otherwise profound topics dealing with mankind's search for enlightenment. In the end it is not merely that these things be represented, they must come together for an exchange of ideas; a growth must occur from this union of minds. New forms must take shape and the flowering of new ideas must yield to the birth of new inspirations and understanding. Creation must occur.

R.S.H.

MUSICAL PERFORMANCE

The Compositional
Hydrolyth

John Zorn

Many good things come with age and for me the most telling has been a certain realisation. An understanding. Not the kind of understanding that happens in the front of your brain, because the most important things in life cannot be grasped in such places. There is a deeper, more intuitive understanding. The understanding that Mysteries, to remain Mysteries, must remain Mysteries, and are not meant to be understood. Unravelled, yes. But never fully, because it is the Mystery itself that is the reality. The Mystery gives birth to the Search, and the Search is life.

Music is one of the great Mysteries. It gives life. It is not a career, nor a business, nor a craft. It is a gift, and a great responsibility.

Because one can never know where the creative spark comes from or why it exists, it must be treasured as Mystery. For the most part I believe that creativity chooses you, not the other way around. When it is with you the universe makes sense and the struggles have meaning. When it leaves there is an emptiness. A void. Meaning eludes you. Simply waiting for its return is painful, and is often exacerbated by very human needs: for shelter, food and drink, a sense of belonging, understanding and love. One can passively exercise patience and wait for visions to return, in the shamanic tradition of incubation as espoused by Empedocles and Parmenides, or one can take action and explore the esoteric traditions that have been used throughout the ages as catalysts for change: Magic, Alchemy, Shamanism and the like. In recent years I have become interested in how these techniques can be used as an aid in compositional practicum.

Through study and transformation, whether it be fasting, ritual, incantation, study, spell, trance or meditation, one can learn to access the power of creativity almost at will. This is not about inducing change through drugs, or altering levels of perception within yourself, but rather about tapping a living energy force that exists at all times everywhere. Call it what you will, Magic, self-hypnosis, alchemical transformation, it is something to be respected, because if it is not taken seriously it can destroy you.

From the sleeve notes to *Magick* (Tzadik).

JOHN ZORN

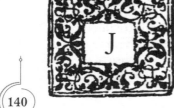

ohn Zorn is an American avant-garde composer, arranger, record producer, saxophonist and multi-instrumentalist. Zorn's recorded output is prolific with hundreds of album credits as a performer, composer, or producer. His work has touched on a wide range of musical genres, often within a single composition, but he is best known for his avant-garde, jazz, improvised and contemporary classical music.

Zorn's sonic explorations into the worlds of magick, alchemy, kaballah and other mystical traditions have astounded listeners for over a decade. His compositions and recorded works dealing with these diverse topics include: *Zohar* (with the Boredom's Yamantaka Eye), *Book of Angels Vol I-X*, *Magick* (with the Necronomicon String Quartet), his Masada group, *Rituals, At The Mountains Of Madness* among many others.

At the core of Zorn's interest in these topics is the concept of what he calls the 'Mystery'. It is this enigma of mysteries that while constantly seeking to be understood can never fully be revealed. Yet in seeking to unravel the core of this Mystery one finds the source of all creativity.

Zorn's compositions and performances instil a vibrant sense of life, an underlying power of being that supersedes the mundane and reaches out to something that exists beyond the everyday. His work, his involvement in the promotion of radical Jewish culture, his interests in the esoteric frameworks that inform his musics, all play into a larger form. A form that when looked at with perspective gives the listener a chance to take in the depth and the breadth of an astounding array of personal philosophical explorations.

That Zorn is a prolific contributor to the advancement of contemporary music is without a doubt. The epic catalogue of his recorded work has reached almost Lovecraftian proportions. A vast series of documents exploring backgrounds, ideas, cultures and musical forms without hesitation.

For this year's Equinox Festival John Zorn will strip bare the form of his personal music, performing for the first time in the UK an astonishing solo saxophone p e r f o r m a n c e e s p e c i a l l y commissioned for the festival. An evening of intimate illumination brought to those present by the power of sonic explorations into the unknown.

141

COMUS

he variables that surround the mystery that is Comus are still mostly unknown. A chilling and thought provoking record released in the early 1970s, followed by a handful of years and a second album and then silence.

During this period of activity they managed to tour with Bowie, leaving an impression on the minds of his fans, creating a mystique as powerful as their namesake, the Greek god for whom John Milton wrote his famous masque.

Over the ensuing years the members had drifted along, continuing to make music, working on various personal projects, oblivious to the growing interest in that rare first album. Decades passed and the legacy of this lost band grew.

Due in part to the increasing ability for access to the records fans have come and word has spread. But in 2008 the final curtain was drawn aside, driven partly through the endeavours of fan Mikael Åkerfeldt (Opeth singer and songwriter), bringing them to the attention of the programmers of the Mellotronen Festival in Sweden. In March of that year Comus took the stage for the first time in 35 years. Bringing back into the light the power of darkness that haunted the lyrical and musical genius of their birth.

Being able to present Comus for their first UK performance in 37 years is an honour and a privilege. Proof that the beauty of their songs and the magnificence of their dramatic, often violent e m o t i o n a l fervour, is still as potent after all these years.

Comus will perform their first album *First Utterance* in its entirety at this year's Equinox Festival.

THRESHOLD HOUSEBOYS CHOIR

Peter Christopherson has played an important role in the evolution of experimental musics over the course of the past three decades. As a founding member of Throbbing Gristle, Coil and Psychic TV, Peter exists in a realm that pushes at the boundaries of musical and spiritual exploration, all the while communicating a distinct mix of, in his own words, 'the sacred and the profane'.

Open about his 'pagan' beliefs, the themes of spiritual discovery and exploration have always been at the forefront of previous projects like Coil. With his solo project Threshold HouseBoys Choir Peter delivers an impactive audio-visual experience. Blending imagery culled from his own experiences as a witness to public rituals in southeast Asia with his signature electronic compositions, Threshold House represents a cumulation of Peter's work over the past three decades.

Prior to his musical career, Peter Christopherson was a commercial artist, designer, and photographer. Notably, he was one of the three partners of the design group Hipgnosis, which was responsible for many classic album covers of the 1970s. Christopherson remained involved with commercial art through his later musical career as a director of music videos and television commercials.

Having 'abandoned the West' Peter now lives in Asia '*way* upriver, deep in the mountainous jungles, shaven headed, musing in the shadows on snails and straight razors, surrounded by a Private Army of young, loyal and bloodthirsty b o d y g u a r d s , waiting to fulfill my every whim, no matter how bizarre, perverted or outlandish.... Well the last part is true anyway!'

145

ÆTHENOR

At the core of Æthenor are a trio of musicians residing in Geneva, Paris and London. Between them they comprise members of of Guapo, Sunn O))), Mothlite, Miasma & the Carousel of Headless Horses, Khanate and Shora.

Æthenor summon the most somnolent examples of Bernard Parmegiani, Organum, Nurse with Wound, Klaus Schulze, Igor Wakhevitch, Coil, Iancu Dumitrescu and Charlemagne Palestine. Acousmatic drones drift into crackling and bubbling sonic clusters. Lulling piano motifs and lamenting chants shimmer into distant lunar horizons while oscillators spin and dive serenely into unchartered audial regions. Sometimes as calm as a silvery sea, so that every gentle cat's-paw and lapping wave is deafening, sometimes as tempestuous as a fuming lava beach, spitting and popping at the surface. Æthenor have unlocked a chamber of arcane and auroral sound that is as incandescent as it is magnetic. Like the moon's pull.

Faking Gold & Murder is the third and latest album by Æthenor. Spectral resonances and reflections create an invisible orchestra around the players, journeying from concrete blast-beats to lunar psych meditations. The precision of process frames the work into a suite of improvised pieces that lean so far away from the stereotype it's hard not to fathom the work as composition. The album features an incandescent vocal performance by David Tibet of Current 93. An immersion into antiquated post-renaissance dreams and perennial philosophy, Tibet heralds a eulogy to a secret history of the 'higher ær'. *Faking Gold & Murder* is by far the most studied and sensitively arranged of all Æthenor's work, its evocative nature being negotiated by a very meticulous sense of ebb and flow.

Æthenor performed a select number of shows in April 2008 including an appearance at the Roadburn Festival (by request of David Tibet) in support of their second album *Betimes Black Cloudmasses*. The line-up, as ephemeral as the music dictates was anchored by the trio of Daniel O'Sullivan, Vincent de Roguin and Stephen O'Malley, and augmented by special guests including UK improvising legend Steve Noble and vocalist Kristoffer Rygg. In constant pursuit of the alchemical process all of the live shows were recorded to multi-track and will no doubt resurface in a distilled form.

T.A.G.C.

The Anti Group Communications

The original idea for the Anti Group was devised by A. Newton and S. J. Turner (R. I. P) in 1978, with the intention of the formation of a multi-dimensional research & development project active in many related areas. Research and Development of sound/film/video/performance and the documentation of each project was the fundamental Modus Operandi. Strictly speaking TAGC are not a group, but a variable collection of individuals contributing under invitation and the directorship of Adi Newton, (Although since the mid 1990,s TAGC has been represented solely by Adi Newton and his partner mullti-media artist Jane Radion-Newton). Underlining this basic idea lays the deeper philosophical and theoretical work of TAGC; the C derived from Communications and to also infers the DNA code of genetics. The primary concern of TAGC is research & development and documentation, also the expanding of the connections and concepts that are explored and experimented with empirically theoretical possibilities and its advancement . Also the expansion of consciousness whether via applied use of computers and audio-visual technology or via arcane systems of magick or other occult or esoteric sciences .

148

Z'EV

Z'EV is an American text-sound artist and mystic who is perhaps best known for his work as a catacoustic (reflected sound-based) percussionist. His work with both text and sound has been influenced by the Middle Eastern mystical system best known as Kabbalah, as well as – but not limited to – African, Afro-Caribbean and Indonesian rhythms, musics and cultures. He has studied Ewe (Ghana) music, Balinese gamelan, and Indian tala. Z'EV does not consider his performances as solos, but rather as the unique inter-reactions between himself and his instruments; the particular physical space of the performance; the particular time and geographic location of the performance; and the energies of the audience.

149

ROB MAZUREK

Rob Mazurek is a sound/vision abstractivist, cornetist, improviser, composer and multimedia artist with a unique style drawing from many facets of contemporary and non-contemporary sound and vision.

Mazurek's work continues to defy simple classification. Often pushing into musical forms beyond his jazz composition background Mazurek's musical groups range from the vast big-band avant ensemble Exploding Star Orchestra, through his own Rob Mazurek Quintet, on to his blisteringly intense solo experimental electronic work.

150

Beyond his musical background Mazurk is a painter and multimedia artist whose work draws heavily on a astounding group of marginal, often esoteric influences.

www.robmazurek.com

DIETER MUH

Dieter Muh exist in a form that has developed itself over the past decade into an exploration of themes inhabiting the realm of what was once called 'industrial' music. The UK-based duo of Dave Uden and Steve Cammack have been experimenting with music and sound art for over a decade.

In the context of contemporary electronic music Dieter Muh represent a bridge between the past and the future. With an astounding amount of unofficial releases on cassette and cdr under their name the pinnacle of their sonic research is the recent collaborative effort with occultist and writer Lon Milo DuQuette – *The Call* released on their own Haemoccult Recordings imprint.

151

The Call is an incredible meshing of the Dieter Muh sound with Lon's distinctive voicing. A truly occult work made by the hands of those who have been ever-present at the doorway to the threshold into the beyond.

K 11 - PIETRO RIPARBELLI

K 11 is a project of Italian sound/installation artist Pietro Riparbelli that deals with the world of radio signals, trans-communication and other invisible phenomena, to create a dimension where the only sound sources are signals from shortwave radio receivers. Riparbelli graduated in Philosophy with a degree in Philosophical Anthropology, and he explores these themes in his work as an artist.

His recent work *Voices from Thelema* is an instrumental trans-communication action with short wave radio receivers realised inside the ruins of Aleister Crowley's famed Thelema Abbey in Cefalù, October 14, 2007.

K 11 now revisits this site and seeks to uncover the *genius loci*, the very essence of the building itself, to reach out into the ether and construct meaning and reality from that which is beyond our grasp.

PESTREPELLER

Pestrepeller are an experimental drone-rock noise group made up of artist and writer Edwin Pouncey (aka Savage Pencil/Sav X), writer, artist, broadcaster and creator of *The Sound Projector* magazine Ed Pinsent, artist and designer Harley Richardson, musician Peter Hope-Evans (of Medicine Head fame) and artist, musician and broadcaster Sharon Gal. Their work has been described as, 'a gem of free-improvised-found sound collage, enriched with pagan folky vibes and supernatural horror Noise, dedicated to H.P. Lovecraft, Clark Ashton Smith and Austin Osman Spare.' To date Pestrepeller have released three full length albums (*Rodent And Insect Eliminator, Nug Yar* and *Isle Of Dark Magick*) and share one side of a limited 12" picture disc with Italian interplanetary sound scientists My Cat Is An Alien. Their fourth album (already recorded) remains 'in the can' until they can find a suitable label to release it into the world.

HATI

HATI is an audiovisual project based on the sound of acoustic instruments: ethnic, hand-made and found objects. HATI connects a personal interest in modern improvised and acoustic music with ritual and meditation. The band have performed many concerts in Poland, Germany, Spain, Netherlands, Belgium, Ireland, Northern Ireland and at festivals including Wroclaw Industrial Festival and Audio Art in Krakow. Nowadays HATI performs as a duo: Rafal X-NAVI Iwanski and Rafal SABON Kolacki, ocasionally with other artists. They are also the organizers of CoCArt Music Festival in Torun, Poland. Live free improvisation performances with (among others): Z'EV, PURE, Robert Curgenven, WEREJU, Andrzej Przybielski, Marcelo Aguirre, Raymond Salvatore Harmon.

www.myspace. com/hatitah

154

KINIT HER

The members of this trio from Wisconsin draw heavily on the symbols of a vast array of mythical and mystical ideologies. Similarly their music finds its currents in a number of interweaving forms including folk, improvised music, psychedelic, metal. Like the evanescent music that accompanies the animated nightmares of the Brothers Quay they make sounds that seem to issue forth from the dark recesses of the subconscious mind.

With backgrounds in esoteric, anthropological and religious studies each member brings to the table a unique voice, both metaphoric and literal. Subtle compositions break way into fields of found sound, folk enchantment yeilds to darker, heavy electronic manipulations. With a surrealistic lyricism often unknown in most contemporary music these ideas coalesce into something startlingly beautiful and nightmarishly haunting.

www.myspace.com/ kinither

BURIAL HEX

Burial Hex is a chthonic composition cycle written in preparation for thee final mysteries in the coming twilight of this Kali Yuga; founded in 2004 by Clay Ruby (Davenport/ Second Family Band, Jex Thoth, Wormsblood, Zodiacs, Rose Croix, others). The Burial Hex cycle has traveled far in the last five years, crafting epic voyages of electro-animist chamber musics, Burial Hex has experimented with everything from dark motorik electro to psychedelic power electronics to post-mortem new age to astral warrior trance; sometimes shifting between several styles within a single composition; often screaming out lyrics inspired by anything from Renaissance poetry to the hallucinations of William Blake and HP Lovecraft to a personal fountain of improvised crypto-mythic poetry. Burial Hex has released a stunning amount of music on limited edition vinyl, CDs, CDRs and cassettes in the underground scene; both solo and in splits or collaborations   with artists such as Sylvester Anfang II, Zola Jesus, Oath, The Mumber Toes, Neutoter Der Plage and Skin Graft; for labels such as Aurora Borealis, SNSE and Cult Cassettes, among others. *www.myspace.com/ burialhex*

156

YAN-GANT-Y-TAN

'Born from the miasma above a Breton marsh, Yan-gant-y-tan, or YGYT ('ye-git') as they are known to their fans, were one of the more incongruous bands to emerge from the French occult music scene of the late 1970s. Isolated somewhat from the Parisian centre, taking their name from a demon spirit of Brittany, Yan-gant-y-tan were able to develop their unique brand of mephitic disco away from the reflected glare of stack heels and bright lipstick so prevalent at the time.

The rustic fug of their rural surroundings, combined with their cultivation of a certain technical rawness, meant that their early music – a gloriously insane attempt to meld grimoiric paraphernalia with primitive motorik dance music – gradually slowed down to a no-less-potent funereal march, which fans have likened to wandering lights over a midnight marsh.'

- from *The Encyclopaedia Of French Occult Rock, 1968 – 1984*, David Wilde

157

At the Equinox Festival, for their first UK gig in three decades, YGYT will perform a triptych of tracks from their one and only recording, *The Mirror Ball Of Solomon*, a ritual delineation and deconstruction of disco ceremonial structured around the little-known 54th degree of Freemasonry.

JAMES FERRARO

James Ferraro is one half of The Skaters, one half of Lamborghini Crystal and the contemporary underground's favourite alchemist, with a wide variety of styles all representing different dreams of a demonic mind tower spanning from freak flesh bodybuilder atmospheres to ambient modern world/psych.

The substance of his music is defined by the interplay of ideas and the transformation of themselves into characters while playing and while living and using the inner dialogue that comes with cognising the symbols of the outside world as a ground for the music to stand.

158

When asked about the purpose of his music, James Ferraro replied 'my life has been a serious journey to spread gnarly vibes. I often think about the sensation of catching a frisbee and I think this sensation is the intersection for the fourth dimension. The fourth dimensional space not clearly seen sticking its face through from a section of space we cannot perceive. And the sensation points me in the direction towards seeing the true relation of things'.

Chaos Majik

CM is the solo project of Todd Brooks, founder of Pendu, an organization based in Brooklyn, NY that promotes occultism, adhocism, and eroticism in the arts. Besides his work in CM, he is also a member of Ghost Moth (with free-jazz legend Daniel Carter) and Abuse Report. CM uses handmade, homebuilt oscillators and feedback-loops to produce hi-frequency analogue tones over a droning low-end for the purpose of arousing visceral and ecstatic, psychical states; exploring uses of ritual in sound and sound in ritual.

Founder of the NY Eye & Ear Festival + Scorpio Cinema as well as a musician, writer, and visual artist. Having published a book of collected poetic-texts entitled *Analekta: Semantic Texts* he is currently working on a non-fiction historical biography tentatively titled *Bouzingo Means Noise!* about a relatively obscure French literary collective from the 19th Century that included some famous figures including Gerard de Nerval, Theophile Gautier, Petrus Borel, and others. Todd is also a regular contributor for the online magazine *Foxy Digitalis*.

RITUAL PERFORMANCE

The Theatre of the Mind

Ritual is one of man's oldest forms of consciousness modification. Through rigorous tests and theatrical experiences man has placed themselves outside of the mundane regularities of everyday life in order that they may achieve communication with the beyond.

From ancient mankind's cryptic cave rituals through Hellenistic rites of passage to the contemporary Catholic mass, the ritual represents our ability to inscribe into our actions the nature of that which is divine.

In approaching the ritual performance the variables are as great as the cultures that have birthed them. Yet something remains in each form that the ritual takes that is a constant, regardless of culture, language or background. That constant is the unifying force in all ritual practice – belief. Belief that one's actions can cause change to occur, belief that will is a force that determines cause, and finally belief that in believing we give the ritual itself purpose.

Yet ritual in all its manifestations is merely the art of performance; a highly choreographed and sophisticated stage play onto which the participants project their emotions and philosophical aspirations in order to delve within themselves. Thus ritual becomes at once an exploration of self and, through group involvement, a unifying form that reinforces the beliefs of the individuals participating in and paying witness to the ritual.

In celebration of the ritual we present artists whose work brings out the very core of contemporary spiritual self discovery. Personal, evocative, often enigmatic, these rituals shed light on the nature of spirituality as it manifests in contemporary society. *R.S.H.*

ARKTAU EOS

Finland's Arktau Eos create the ritual experience in a live setting like no other group working today. Part contemporary ritual, part shamanic workout, they hail from the northernmost extremes of arctic night, describing their present work as 'a gnarled old tree telling you of worlds beyond, roots nestled in the constellations above and branches flowering in vaulted tombs below.' Utilising electro-acoustic musical instrumentation and other media, the vision they weave together is unsettling, yet ultimately beautiful.

Since the inception of Arktau Eos in 2005, their publicly seen side has involved performances in Finland, U.K., and the Russian Federation, three albums (the latest a double-album) and visual documentation.

161

Barry William Hale's
NOKO

Noko is the performative aspect of Barry William Hale's various lines of esoteric research, involving long standing collaborations, erupting into what is traditionally a fine arts arena. Their merging of magical ritual work with contemporary experimental sound and vision forms highly original assemblages in a live multimedia format.

Although the Enochian Magical system has been a prominent focus, other directions have included Sonic Magical investigations of the Qlipotic genii and the upcoming 'Conjuration of Beelzebub'. Noko, while varied in its associated personnel, has produced a consistent, documented body of work since 1993. The Equinox Festival line-up also features long time member Scott Barnes (sound realisation) and Michael Strum (visualist).

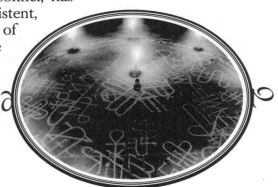

Raymond Salvatore Harmon

Currently residing in London, Raymond Salvatore Harmon is a cross genre media artist, filmmaker, sound artist, and record producer whose work defies categorisation. As a new media artist and experimental filmmaker his work combines anthropological study, philosophic discourse, and contemporary art. His CV extends from performance based 16mm and 8mm film to video circuit-bending and analog feedback installations as well as sound and visual conceptual installations and guerrilla media actions.

163

Over the past decade Harmon has developed theoretical and practical applications for the use of Transcendental Cinema in occult ritual. Utilising mystical and occult texts as subliminal content within an experimental m e d i a f r a m e w o r k , H a r m o n ' s occult based films redefine ritual for a contemporary audience.

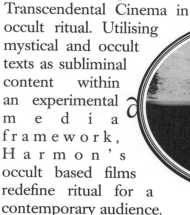

LECTURES & PRESENTATIONS

164

The Power of the Word:
Learning as an Active Experience.

Education via an oral tradition predates the written word. Before print or even practical writing societies transferred knowledge of all kinds via story telling, parable, and song. Those to whom such an oral tradition was entrusted were the first scholars, priests and shaman of the world's cultures. No less today the speakers of the world truly emphasise the importance of hearing someone speak publicly about a given topic.

Within the esoteric traditions the need for direct communication between teacher and student is often overlooked. Relying on published text and related documentation the student of contemporary mysticism is often at a distance from those whose deeper and personal knowledge of a given topic would benefit the learning and growing process.

The ability to hear and question the speaker is of utmost importance in the path toward knowing. Questioning, helping to refine the details of a specific idea, allows one to grasp the totality of the concept that may be only alluded to in a text. It is this questioning, this deeper probing of thought and exchange of ideas from which understanding is born. Without the direct abilty to question and listen to the progenitor of an idea (be they teacher, artist or philosopher) the learning process becomes thin, without depth or meaning.

165

The enrichment of the mind must come from communication, and such communication must not be one way, but an exchange that develops and grows, as do the student and the teacher. Such quantifiable exchange gives perspective, and without perspective how can one be expected to grow?

By presenting a broad range of speakers and lecturers whose presentations and workshops give the audience a more hands-on and direct analysis of thought and form the Equinox Festival provides a platform through which learning becomes a participatory event. Engaging both the speaker and the audience in an exchange of ideas in order to fuel the birth of creative expression.
R.S.H.

Ralph Metzner

Alchemical Divination –
Remembering the Past, Envisioning Possible Futures

Alchemy, like shamanism and yoga, with which it is related, involves teachings and practices of physical, psychic and spiritual transformation. Divination is the practice of seeking healing and spiritual guidance from inner sources of wisdom and knowledge.

Alchemical divinations are processes of structured intuitive inquiry, using light-fire yoga methods for a mildly expanded state of consciousness. We work in the spirit of the ancient Roman deity Janus, god of doorways, passages and transitions, whose two faces look in a balanced way into the past and the future.

The basic purpose of the alchemical divination processes is to help individuals obtain problem resolution and visionary inspiration for their life path in its interpersonal, professional, creative and spiritual dimensions. Using focused meditative regression, we can connect with unresolved and incomplete aspects of our past, especially in the formative years of childhood and youth, to 're-member' and integrate those into our present sense of who we are. This leads to a deepened sense of self and its history, and greater freedom to make healthy and authentic choices in the present. Using focussed meditative visioning, we can search along the probability time-lines for guidance about our probable and possible futures – in work, relationships, creativity and spiritual growth. This leads to a heightened sense of self and its potentials, and greater power to realise our highest spiritual aspirations.

Ralph Metzner, Ph.D. is a recognized   pioneer in studies of consciousness and transformation. Educated at Oxford and Harvard, he collaborated with Timothy Leary and Richard Alpert in studies with psychedelics at Harvard in the 1960s, co-authoring *The Psychedelic Experience*. He is a psychotherapist and Professor Emeritus at the California Institute of Integral Studies. He is also cofounder/president of the Green Earth Foundation, dedicated to 'healing and harmonising the relations between humanity, Earth and Spirit.' His books include *The Well of Remembrance*, *The Unfolding Self* and *Green Psychology*; and a new series of short books on The Ecology of Consciousness.

ERIK DAVIS

Ph A Brief History of the antasm

The phantasm is an image with a life of its own. Possessing more substance than a daydream but less than the kitchen sink, the phantasm flits about the liminal zone between mind and nature, the subconscious and the super-conscious, the body and the spirit. Magic and dream and astral travel and shamanic voyaging are all arts of the phantasm, a normally excluded category of reality that actually inhabits the heart of our condition. Tracing ancient theories of perception and memory, Erik Davis will frame the phantasm as the 'excluded middle' of the visionary imagination, the bridge between dimensions and realms of explanation. Despite its tricky character, the delusions it bears with its gifts, the phantasm beckons us through and between the Scylla and Charabdis of New Age supernaturalism and disenchanted materialism.

The phantasm is not static, but like the idea of the imagination itself, transforms in the face of historical change, and especially changes in media technology, medical models, and the philosophy of perception. Today philosophers continue to wrestle with the phantasm in its ambiguous guise as the simulacrum, while chaos magicians loose the image from inherited structures of meaning and allow it to mutate. Meanwhile, the explosion of new media and post-cinematic technologies, as well as the sophistication of contemporary technologies of perception management, have created an environment where the nature of reality itself begins to take on the haunting character of the phantasm.

Erik Davis is a San Francisco-based writer, performer, and independent scholar. He is the author of *TechGnosis: Myth, Magic, and Mysticism in the Age of Information* (Harmony), *The Visionary State: A Journey through California's Spiritual Landscape* (Chronicle), and a 33 1/3 volume on the occult dimensions of *Led Zeppelin IV* (Continuum,). Davis has contributed to scores of magazines and books, and has taught at UC Berkeley, UC Davis, the Maybe Logic Academy, and the California Institute of Integral Studies. He wrote the libretto for the Burning Man rock opera How to Survive the Apocalypse, and he posts sometimes at *techgnosis.com*.

DAVID BETH

A-Mor:

A gnostic magician's view on esoteric love and eros

In this lecture, David Beth will speak on the importance, possibilities and dangers of love and eros in the context of magical and esoteric work. Drawing on initiatic knowledge and experience from his work in the Voudon Gnostic orders of Michael Bertiaux, the Fraternitas Borealis and Ecclesia Gnostica Aeterna, David will venture into controversial territory to expound powerful visions of love and eros vital to the work of initiates.

(170)

David Beth, author of *Voudon Gnosis,* is a writer and esoteric explorer. He was born to German parents in Luanda, Angola, May 1974. In the course of his life he spent 16 years in Africa living in Nigeria and Kenya. The unique, rich metaphysical and spiritual climate of Africa has had a   huge influence on David from a very young age. During these 16 years he was fortunate to encounter personally many powerful representatives of the local spiritual and metaphysical traditions such as Susanne Wenger, high priestess of Osun and keeper of the sacred groves of Oshogbo. In his years in Africa he has received transmissions and empowerments of various types which he has infused in his magical and spiritual work.

EDWIN POUNCEY

Ira Cohen:
A Magickal Vision

Pouncey's fascination with Cohen's extraordinary life and admiration for his art and ideas produced several articles about him for *The Wire* magazine, and it is material from these (together with an appraisal of Cohen's magickal vision) that will form the basis of Pouncey's lecture for this year's Equinox Festival.

171

Born in Leeds, West Yorkshire, Edwin Pouncey has worked as a music journalist since the early '80s, where he has been fortunate enough to meet and talk with many important musicians and artists. After joining *The Wire* magazine in the mid-'90s on a freelance basis, he was given the opportunity to speak to some major figures of the '60s and '70s counterculture – including New York poet, filmmaker, publisher and shaman Ira Cohen whose mylar photographs were used for album sleeves by Spirit, John McLaughlin and Pharaoh Sanders and on paperback book covers for William S. Burroughs Jr. and science fiction writer A.E. Van Vogt.

KENDALL GEERS

Kendell Geers is a South African born installation and media artist whose celebration of the violent undertones of contemporary society reflect a growing concern with the lack of attention paid to issues that are often ignored by the public eye.

Geers creates work that aims to disrupt commonly accepted moral codes and principles. Employing a wide range of references - from the realms of history of art, pornography, iconography and kitsch - Geers questions artistic value and mocks the notion of originality. His work reveals razor-sharp humour that plays with the viewer's repulsion and ridicules racial or religious stereotypes. Laden with complex and deep political implications, it is challenging and confrontational. At the same time, Geers' minimalist aesthetics generate a subtle poetic undertone.

His longstanding relationship with various esoteric traditions is often overlooked in the critical assessment of his body of work. This relationship yields an insightful, often profound, depth that is reveled in the subtle underpinnings of his creations.

PHILIP H. FARBER

Gods, Demons & Imaginary Friends
(Whether You Believe in Them or Not)

Did you know that recent discoveries concerning human neurology suggest that the magical operation of evocation – contacting and communicating with spirits – has a biological basis? Our gods, demons, angels, loas, and imaginary friends are there for reasons beyond the obvious. Come and learn new, exciting, and practical ways to play with and learn from our less corporeal colleagues. Phil will offer discussion, demonstration and fun group participation to illustrate these important magical ideas.

173

Philip H. Farber is the author of *Futureritual: Magick for the 21st Century*, a manual of neurological exploration and *Meta-Magick:The Book of Atem* (Weiser Books, 2008). His articles on magick and popular culture have appeared in *Green Egg Magazine*, *The Journal of Hypnotism*, *Hypnosis Today*, *Mondo 2000*, *High Times*, *Paradigm Shift*, *Reality Sandwich* and other unique publications and web sites. He has produced several DVD packages on magical topics, including *Magick for the 21st Century* and *Meta-Magick INVOCATION.* Phil is an instructor for Maybe Logic Academy (*www.maybelogic.org*), a Certified Hypnotist and a Licensed Trainer of Neuro-linguistic Programming, with a private practice in New York's Mid-Hudson Valley.

Visit Phil at *www.hawkridgeproductions.com*.

MARCO PASI

Marco Pasi is Assistant Professor in History of Hermetic philosophy and related currents. He holds an MA in Philosophy from the University of Milan, and a PhD in Religious studies from the Ecole Pratique des Hautes Etudes (Sorbonne, Paris). He has focussed his research mainly on the relationship between modern esotericism and politics, on the history of the idea of magic, and on methodological issues related to the study of Western esotericism. He is a member of the editorial board of *Aries: Journal for the Study of Western Esotericism and Politica Hermetica.*

174

Pasi spent a period studying at the Warburg Institute (London) in 2000, and was Lecturer for History of European esoteric currents at the EPHE from 2001 to 2004. In 2004 he was appointed Assistant Professor for History of Western Esotericism since the 19th century at the University of Amsterdam. Pasi is particularly interested in the processes of transformation of esotericism after the Enlightenment, especially under the impact of secularisation and modernisation, and the relationship between esoteric currents and the wider cultural context in which they have developed.

ROBERT WALLIS

'Remember Mugwort, what you made known':
The Nine Herbs Charm, Mugwort Lore and Elf-persons – an animic approach to Anglo-Saxon Magick

Mugwort (*Artemesia vulgaris*) is a common wayside herb which is easily overlooked, but it occurs frequently in the folklore of the northern hemisphere as a special plant. Moreover, it is inscribed with considerable importance as the 'mother' and 'oldest' of herbs, linked also to elves, healing, magic and the god Woden, in the tenth century Anglo-Saxon spellbook *Lacnunga* (Leech-book). My research on Anglo-Saxon paganism marks out Mugwort as a key power-plant to Anglo-Saxon shaman/magicians, and my experiments also indicate that Mugwort is an entheogen or mind-alterant. An animistic reading of these insights has implications for understanding Anglo-Saxon paganism and for magicians working in the Northern tradition today. For animists, the world is filled with persons, only some of whom are human and all things – all persons – are connected. Treated respectfully, Mugwort assists human-persons in the adjusted styles of communication (ASC's) required to engage, dialogue and negotiate with other persons – from plants and stones to elves and deities – and to 'see as others do'.

175

Robert J. Wallis PhD teaches on visual and material culture at Richmond University, London, where he coordinates the MA Art History. He also teaches for the Open University and is a visiting researcher in archaeology at Southampton University. His research interests range from art in archaeological and anthropological contexts, to the representation of the past, particularly among today's pagans. With Jenny Blain, he directs the *Sacred Sites, Contested Rites/Rights Project*, examining pagan engagements with prehistoric monuments and other archaeology.

CARL ABRAHAMSSON

Size Matters

We're squeezed inbetween perspectives, and as these vary and fluctuate, so does the level of clarity of thinking. A perception of increased speed can, possibly, be manipulated by classical modes of spiritually connected behaviour (meditation, yoga et al). It only solves the problem on an individual level though. The connected perspective, the here and now, is steadily becoming smaller and faster. Everything and everyone is fragmented for purposes of control and consumerism. What are the implications of new technology vis-à-vis the human brain? The disconnected perspective becomes more and more problematic, and the related holistic perspective one of scorn and ridicule. Can humans still be humans in an existence infected by technology? What will the future be like, post-technology? Is spirituality a viable key to the solution? These and many other aspects of a very problematic issue will be the subject of Carl Abrahamsson's pro-human speech.

Carl Abrahamsson is a multidisciplinary witness to the current cultural question marks around us. Embarking on a wide-eyed spiritual journey in his early teens, he has since then been churned through a multitude of teachings by various enlightened beings. His metaphysical interests of yesteryear have more and more become integrated in various artistic expressions, mainly writing, music and photography. Art, according to Abrahamsson, has unlimited talismanic potential, which means, perhaps, that it could be high time to start moving and shaking NOW.

www.carlabrahamsson.com

PAOLA IGLIORI

Writer, publisher, filmmaker and poet Paola Igliori's first book *Entrails, Heads and Tails* (photographic essays and conversations with artists Louise Bourgeois, James Turrell, Enzo Cucchi, Vito Acconci, Cy Twombly, Gilbert & George, Francesco Clemente, Sigmar Polke, Julian Schnabel, Wolfgang Laib) is an exploration of the roots of creativity through the everyday life. She is the author of *American Magus – Harry Smith, a Modern Alchemist,* the superb biography of an influential film maker, ethnomusicologist, anthropologist, painter, magician. Since 2003 Paola Igliori has returned to Italy and founded Villa Lina Bio-Officina a multidisciplinary and multicultural association that holds seminars, conferences and creative activities on her family estate Villa Lina, near Ronciglione in Etruscan Tuscia north of Rome.

177

Paola continues to film the Italian ecstatic and healing dances *Tammorriate, Pizziche* and *Tarante* – broadening the research on the ancient snake of ecstatic and healing music which unwinds through Africa and the Mediterranean. Starting in Morocco in 1990, after having being introduced by Paul Bowles to the various fraternities (Sufi et al) of ecstatic dance and of trance healing: the Jillala, which bring to trance through flute music; the Joujouka autocthonous Berbers, who use archaic wind instruments like Pan's flute, and whose sounds and ceremonial goat skins   recall our Sardinian Mammutones, then finally the Gnawas. In 2007 while filming the African Sufi Fraternity of the Baye Fall she met and married Massamba Fall Sy, a member of this fraternity.

MASSAMBA FALL

Massamba Fall Sy was born in Dakar, Senegal in 1979. In 1998 he entered the Sufi Confraternity Baye Fall founded in Senegal around 1882 by the Mystic Sufi Mame Cheikh Ibrahima Fall called The Light, who dedicated his life of Devotion in Action to Cheikh Amadou Bamba founder of the Holy City of Touba and powerful spiritual voice against Colonialism.

Massamba, left his professional school, to dedicate himself totally to Baye Fall life, beginning to carve prayer rosaries in ebony as Meditation in Action and singing the name of God dancing in circle until dawn.

178

The Baye Fall, African Sufis, put together ecstatic devotion and action with efforts that are sometimes almost superhuman, in their coral work for the community,

In 2007 Massamba meets and marries in Dakar writer and filmmaker Paola Igliori and starts filming *The Seed of Joy* which previewed in 2008 at the Rome Film Festival .

Together they established a centre and guesthouse at Abene in the forest of Casamance, Senegal – Keur Baye Fall – which provides Ecotourism and workshops. They also founded ACKPRODUCTIONS a nonprofit group with many projects of real exchange.

www.ackproductions.com

AARON GACH

Revolutionary Breakthroughs in Extra-Sensory Perception
or: How to do Magic(k) in a Police State

Aaron Gach, Co-founder and Director of Operations for the Center for Tactical Magic, will be presenting a rather vulgar analysis of magic(k) as it applies to art, politics, technology, and social transformation. Leaning (perhaps a bit too heavily) on adventures from the Tactical Magic trenches, this presentation aims to pull the curtain aside and expose a few of the illusions being cast daily within the current global theatre of conflict. By looking at a few of the ways in which old, familiar magical themes have been reconfigured in contemporary society, this talk will attempt to map a trajectory for applied magic(k) that actively intervenes in and recalibrates consensus reality. Ranging from the alchemy of sabotage to the ceremony of street protests and beyond, the presentation will not indulge in wishful thinking. On the contrary, change and effect come to bear only when philosophy is a subjective proposition, desire and praxis that are applied to the event. In this way 'magical thinking' drops its cloak of transcendental escapism and materialises as a political counterperception – an alternative worldview that summons the creative and prophetic power of the multitude and necessitates everyday acts of creative engagement in order to realise positive social transformation.

179

Cultivating mirth and mystery in all four hemispheres, the Center for Tactical Magic began in 2000 as a think-tank dedicated to the research, development, and deployment of all types of magic(k) in the service of positive social transformation. By working across barriers of contemporary art, martial arts, magical arts, and community action, the Center for Tactical Magic has endeavoured to produce numerous public projects that analyse existing forces and activate latent energies. Embracing magical thinking and unconventional uses of technology, the Center for Tactical Magic continues to mix elements of subculture, social politics, and revelry into a powerful potion. To find out more, check out *www.tacticalmagic.org*

ROBERT ANSELL

Adventures in Limbo:
exploring the creative sorcery of
Austin Osman Spare's magico-aesthetic.

In this multimedia lecture Robert Ansell goes back to the original source, developing the themes introduced in The Cult of One (2007) to offer us fresh insights into the theory and technique of Austin Osman Spare's creative sorcery. Here Spare's philosophy of the 'Neither-Neither' is explored in depth through the artist's own words and images. It emerges not as an abstract, but as the artist's primary magical methodology. Supported by the findings of modern cognitive science, the creative processes Spare developed and employed will resonate with writers, artists and musicians who aim to evoke the presence of the otherworldly through their work.

Robert Ansell is widely recognised as a pioneer in the contemporary revolution in talismanic publishing, having co-founded the esoteric fine press Fulgur Limited in 1992. Working closely with Kenneth and Steffi Grant, Michael Bertiaux and the late Andrew Chumbley, he has helped birth some of the most inspirational magical books of recent times. A specialist in the art and sorcery of Austin Osman Spare, his published work includes; *AOS Ex-Libris* (1988), *The Book of Ugly Ecstasy* (1996), *Borough Satyr* (2005) and *The Valley of Fear* (2008). Rarely seen as a public lecturer, his two recent appearances concerning *Spare, AOS: A Celebration* (2006) and <u>*The Cult of One*</u> (2007) were critically acclaimed.

STEPHEN GRASSO

Open Up the Gate

The crossroads is a magical symbol of ingress and egress between worlds and the interplay of spirit and matter. Virtually every culture recognises the crossroads as a holy site associated with magic, witchcraft and strange transitions into the beyond. The crossroads is a metaphor for all of the choices we may be presented with in life, and any physical location where several roads meet is a living storehouse of this potentiality. In Voodoo, Papa Legba is the Saint of the Crossroads, controlling and directing all spiritual traffic. A good relationship with Legba is essential to exploring the mysteries of Voodoo, and such a relationship is only developed by putting in the hours at your local crossroads and inhabiting your patch as a magician. In this way the pulse of magic erupts in the urban landscape, and the end of your street is transformed into a living temple to the mysteries.

181

Stephen Grasso is a writer and artist whose work explores the idea of magic, its history and what it means in the context of the 21st century world. His main focus of interest is African and African Diaspora magico-religious traditions; although his work is also concerned with the way in which a living tradition of magic has survived in the margins of western culture as a liminal thread throughout history. His writing appears in the anthologies Generation Hex, Dreamflesh, and Devoted. He is currently working on a book about his personal experiences exploring magic, occultism, Voodoo and related marginalised belief systems. He is a founder and regular contributor to *liminalnation.org*.

ORRYELLE
DEFENESTRATE-BASCULE

Time, Fate
& Spider Magicks

At the Equinox Festival Orryelle will be speaking about Time, Fate and Spider Magicks. The dichotomy of fate and will shall be explored, including the relationship of destiny with True Will, and the anima/animus as Holy Guardian Angel. The Web of Wyrd or Tapestry of Fate is investigated as a model for mapping interconnectivity and initiating astral timetravel within the microcosm of one's magick circle. Archetypes worked with will include Kali as birther and devourer of Time and The Three Fates, Moerae or Norns as arachnean deities of Fate and Time spinning weaving and cutting the intertwined strands of our lifelines, and the mysterious Fourth Fate.

182

This talk will include poetic readings from Orryelle's *Book of the Spider* and other inspired writings. It will be as much a performance as a speech, including harmonic chanting, magickal movement, mudra and verse.

Orryelle Defenestrate-Bascule is the director of the Australian-based Metamorphic Ritual Theatre Co., artist-author of *CONJUNCTIO*, a Graphic Grimmoire from Fulgur Limited, *The Book of Kaos Tarot* and *A Brief HIRStory of TimEmiT*... Orryelle is an initiated Tantric Aghori and founder of the HermAphroditic ChAOrder of the Silver Dusk.

PAUL DEVEREUX

Rock Music for Real
Sound at Sacred Places

Paul Devereux presents a powerful audio-visual presentation on the new science of 'archaeoacoustics' – the study of sound at archaelogical sites. Over the course of almost an hour, we'll visit places as different as remote American Indian vision quest sites, ancient Mayan, Egyptian, Greek and Indian temples, and British Stone Age monuments, and we'll listen in to some of them too! We'll learn how Stone Age knowledge can perhaps guide modern laboratory work on the brain, and hear a clip of Z'EV playing the rocks at the Welsh source of the Stonehenge bluestones. You thought you knew rock music? You ain't heard anything yet...

Paul Devereux is a research associate at the Royal College of Art, London, investigating with Jon Wozencroft (Touch Music) the audio-visual characteristics of the Avebury Neolithic complex, Wiltshire, U.K., and the Preseli area of Wales, U.K., source of the Stonehenge bluestones, and is a founding co-editor of the peer-reviewed publication, *Time & Mind: The Journal of Archaeology, Consciousness and Culture* (Berg, Oxford). He is a Fellow of the Royal Society of Arts and a Senior Research Fellow of International Consciousness Research Laboratories (ICRL), Princeton. Over a period of nearly 30 years he has written or co-written some 26 books for general readerships, primarily on archaeological and anthropological themes. He has written many articles for both popular and specialist publications, together with a range of academic papers. His research interests focus especially on archaeoacoustics, the prehistoric mind, the anthropology of consciousness, and the origins of art. He is also a painter and photographer.

www.pauldevereux.co.uk

MATTHEW WILEY

AXIS MUNDI:
Pulling Power from the World Tree

Thinking in symbols is the natural order of the mind. The magician-shaman and the like use symbols as a means to elevate consciousness, unhinge the mundane mind, or move to a symbol -specific domain to carry out ones desired work.

From time immemorial under many a name and guise, the Axis Mundi or 'world tree' is a symbol that has been the basis of occult study and philosophical speculation, springing forth from the dawn of time. The Axis Mundi as a symbol proper, begins with the vertical line in which we can explore the ascent and descent of the natural harmony or structure of the universe. The line precedes the circle, thus we have circle and circumference, the beginning and end of all things known and unknown. The line is the first hieroglyph from whence archeology, science, and possibly religion originate.

Matthew Wiley has been teaching traditional Tantra, Yoga, Western Occultism, and comparative religion for more than 10 years. His spiritual quest has led him globetrotting throughout Asia and Europe. Along with studies in Kaula Tantra, and Shamanism, he has worked with Santo Daime, The Native American Church and has lived in several monasteries. As a neophyte ethnobotanist his current focus is on indigenous cultures, the ritual use of psychoactive plants, and their magnitude and importance to the world today. He holds a Yoga Shiromani and is an Initiate in Western Esoterica.

TRANSCENDENTAL CINEMA

Cinema, Myth
& the Mystical Experiencce

186

On the edge of the beyond is a figure we fantasise and project ourselves onto – an avatar as much as a teacher. Both as an externalisation of ourselves and a figure to whom we may seek answers from, this traveller has gone before us, and in doing so has carved a path into the unknown in whose footsteps we may follow. Be they mystic, shaman, kabbalist, sufi, gnostic or countless others we follow them as they have gone from unknowing to knowing and we ourselves seek the route by which they have gained access to the universal light.

Yet enlightenment, in all of its myriad of forms, comes not to those who seek a path trodden by others, but to those that walk where no mind has trod, mapping reality and experience as an art form. Living life, and in doing so, causing change to occur.

Yet the lives of those who journey on a path toward light hold similar patterns, causes and effects that come to place in the shape of the traveler's lifespan that are paralleled in many individual lives.

Much of our perception of a system of thought, be it spiritual or otherwise, is shaped by the idea and impression we have in ourselves of who the creator, the originator of this system is or was. Over time we come to idolise the creator until eventually, generation per generation we worship them. As they have come before us we perceive them as we would any god of antiquity. Timeless, without beginning or end.

But at some point these mystics lived and breathed, ate and slept and above all experienced life. The world inhabited by the journeyers who have gone before us was full of experiences that shaped the path of there knowing. Opening them to ideas and understanding, broadening there perceptions until wisdom finally could occur. These things, stories and ideas, may interest many who would venture on such a path themselves.

And so, in an age when cinema is a dominant form of both artistic expression and educational documentation, we have a programme that incorporates both sides of the journey to knowing. One side tells of the lives and ideas of some of those who in our world are seeking or those who have sought and found. The other films in the program are not so biographical, yet tend toward the practical application of the transcendental experience in the lives of those who may seek the light.

Thus cinema moves into the realm of the spiritual experiences more from familiarity than anything else. We have come to know its flickering ways, to listen to its lies and to believe its illusions. So it is in fact the great tool we possess in preparing the mind for the journey ahead. That we may use cinema not just to learn about those who have departed from the cloud of unknowing, but that we may ourselves find the path that will lets us join them.
R.S.H.

DeZ Vylenz
MINDSCAPE OF ALAN MOORE

A psychedelic journey with the world's most critically acclaimed and widely admired creator of graphic novels, a contemporary shaman with the power to transform consciousness and society.

In *The Mindscape of Alan Moore* we see a portrait of the artist as contemporary shaman, someone with the power to transform consciousness by means of manipulating language, symbols and images.

The film leads the audience through Moore's world with the writer himself as guide, beginning with his childhood background, following the evolution of his career as he transformed the comics medium, to his immersion in a magical worldview where science, spirituality and society are part of the same universe.

Ira Cohen
KINGS WITH STRAW MATS

'The naked Nagas marching to the river, like sparks from some primordial fire, the people of dust with arms held high. There is a pleasure of being mad that only the madman knows.' Ira Cohen

A pilgrimage into the heart of India's greatest sacred celebration, the Kumbh Mela which takes place every 12 years. Filmmaker and poet Ira Cohen brings us face to face with an unforgettable gathering of holy men and into the heart of a visionary experience by rendering it as it really is: a circus of high madness, true devotion and showbiz savvy. The Kumbh Mela takes its name from the Hindu legend which tells how four drops of the gods holy elixir fell to the earth from a 'kumbh' or pitcher during a struggle with jealous demons fighting in the heavens. The celebration takes place where those drops fell to the earth.

189

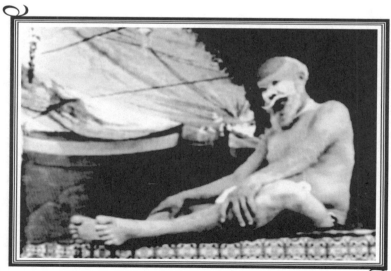

8 Circuit
TIMOTHY LEARY
MODEL OF CONSCIOUSNESS

The 8-Circuit Model of Consciousness is a theory of consciousness first proposed by psychologist Timothy Leary. It models the mind as a collection of 8 'circuits', with each circuit representing a higher stage of evolution than the one before it.

Leary constructed the model based on the lateralisation of brain function. The first four levels, which Leary presumed to reside in the left lobe of the cerebrum, are concerned with the survival of organisms on earth; the other four, which Leary suggested are found in the right lobe, are for use in the future evolution of humans, and remain dormant in the majority of human beings.

190

James Ferraro
Diminishing Shrine Recycles

James Ferraro is a rarity in the contemporary music world. As a musician his work is often defined as experimental, increasingly bordering on the ritualistic.

This film is practically unknown, even among the most die-hard of fans. Released in an edition of 8 copies on VHS it represents a crossroads, where Ferraro's work breaks through the threshold of sonic involvement and delves into the abstract subconscious imagery.

A fully realised visual equivalent to his audio work, *Diminishing Shrine Recycles* represents an astounding step in the direction of filmmaking for this young artist.

MASSAMBA FALL
THE SEED OF JOY

The Baye Fall, African Sufis, put together ecstatic devotion and action with efforts that are sometimes almost superhuman, in their coral work for the community, In 2007 Massamba meets and marries in Dakar writer and filmmaker Paola Igliori and starts filming *The Seed of Joy* which previewed in 2008 at the Rome Film Festival .

Together they have established a centre and guesthouse at Abene, in the forest of Casamance, Senegal : Keur Baye Fall which provides Ecotourism and workshops. They also founded ACKPRODUCTIONS a nonprofit with many projects of real exchange.

192

Paola Igliori
American Magus

Harry Smith, legendary creator of the 1952 Folkways Records Anthology of American Folk Music, was also an artistic giant who was awarded a Guggenheim grant in 1950 for his non-objective films and paintings, an outsider anthropologist who ingested everything from peyote to string figures, a profound and groundbreaking collector who sought out the parallel patterns of multivaried things to get at their inner language, the scariest and most knowledgeable occultist you'll ever know, a friend and mentor of everyone from Allen Ginsberg to Robert Frank, and infinitely more.

Now poet and filmmaker Paola Igliori, who was alone with Smith when he died, has created the first feature-length documentary investigation of this incredible creative presence a live tribute to this unclassifiable classifier, featuring interviews with Allen Ginsberg, Robert Frank, Jonas Mekas, and many others, images from his films, from his infinite collections, diagrams of multiple synthesis of the most varied creative activities, a kaleidoscopic collage of interviews, evocations, and rare archival materials that opens many curiously marked doors in the macrocosm and the microcosm

193

CRAIG BALDWIN
MOCK UP ON MU

A radical hybrid of sci-fi, spy, Western, and even horror genres, Craig Baldwin's *Mock Up On Mu* cobbles together a feature-length "collage-narrative' based on (mostly) true stories of California's post-War sub-cultures of rocket pioneers, alternative religions, and Beat lifestyles. Pulp-serial snippets, industrial-film imagery, and B – and Z – fiction clips are intercut with newly shot live-action material, powering a playful, allegorical trajectory through the now-mythic occult matrix of Jack Parsons (Crowleyite founder of the Jet Propulsion Lab), L.Ron Hubbard (sci-fi author turned cult-leader), and Marjorie Cameron (bohemian artist and 'mother of the New Age movement'). Their intertwined tales spin out into a speculative farce on the militarisation of space, and the corporate take-over of spiritual fulfillment and leisure-time.

194

HARRY SMITH
HEAVEN & EARTH MAGIC

Harry Smith describes *Film #12 (Heaven and Earth Magic)* as follows,

'The first part depicts the heroine's toothache consequent to the loss of a very valuable watermelon, her dentistry and transportation to heaven. Next follows an elaborate exposition of the heavenly land, in terms of Israel, Montreal and the second part depicts the return to Earth from being eaten by Max Muller on the day Edward the Seventh dedicated the Great Sewer of London.'

One of Smith's most admired works; this black and white collage film, prepared from cut-outs from nineteenth-century catalogues, traverses the landscape of an hermetic dream.

195

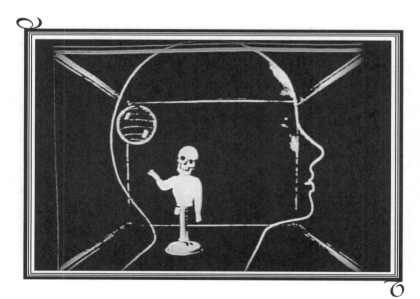

ALEJANDRO JODOROWSKY
THE HOLY MOUNTAIN

Awakening from a comatose sleep and covered in insects, a bearded thief (Horácio Salinas) is almost crucified by children but is rescued by an amputee dwarf. After he and the dwarf share a joint, they travel through scene after scene of surreal images. They wander into a town populated by freaks, fascists, hookers, and religious fanatics, where skinned, crucified livestock are paraded down the street. Costumed frogs and iguanas bloodily reenact the Spanish conquest of South America, innocent people are massacred, and birds fly out of their bullet wounds as soldiers of this Mexican police state rape peasant women for the benefit of tourists who photograph these horrific tableaux. The thief gets drunk with Roman soldiers who proceed to use his body as a mould to create hundreds of kitschy Christ statues. He returns to the street and, with the aid of a fistful of balloons, he rises to the top of tower where he encounters 'The Master', an alchemist (Jodorowsky). The alchemist demonstrates his transformational prowess by turning the thief's excrement into crystals and gold.

Maya Deren
Divine Horsemen:
The Living Gods of Haiti

In 1947 filmmaker Maya Deren received the first Guggenheim Fellowship for creative work in motion pictures based on a proposal for a film on Haitian dance. On trips to Haiti in 1947, 1949 and 1954, she shot several thousand feet of 'Voudoun' rituals. (Creole usage by Deren). Deren had previously advanced her craft as a filmmaker and artist by applying principles of Gestalt psychology, duration and a 'mythical method' to the newest art instrument of the 20th Century. A creative work was the sum of its parts where in assemblage something new was formed making it a 'volatile whole', the foundation of Deren's film work until she arrived in Haiti. Here she reworked her conceptual framework in order to 'render' the logic of Voudoun without manipulation.

Excerpts from: *An Anagram of the Ideas of Filmmaker Maya Deren* © Moira Sullivan, 1997

RAYMOND SALVATORE HARMON
YHVH

YHVH is a tool for transcendental expansion. Non-denominational, non specific (other than in name) to any religion, and free from figurative icons.

Because the nature of the abstract imagery used in YHVH tends toward an interpretive logic, much like a Rorschach test, the imagery becomes personally interpretive. The mind attempts to force some logic on the shifting lights and darks and thus gives us access to the architecture of the subconscious. It is a window into the abstract.

This version of YHVH is *Chokmah*, the soundtrack was created by Rob Mazurek. There are 10 versions, each with its own soundtrack created by a different composer.

KATHRYN FERGUSON

LE BETE

During the summer of 2008 filmmaker Kathryn Ferguson spent three weeks in the Land's End area of Cornwall. During that time she spent a lot of time exploring the ancient stone circles and landmarks including the healing wells at Madron. She felt a total affinity with the landscape and became very drawn to the area, returning many times over the following months. The ancient pagan sites there evoked a similar response in her to those she had grown up with in Ireland. The feeling of ancient ritual and that the land was sacred inspired her desire to make a film expressing this.

This coincided with an art gallery called the T1+2 Gallery commissioning her to make a film for a group show called 'Le Bete'. The show was to be based around the 1975 film of the same name by Walerian Borowczyk. The film focuses on the theme of bestiality. She began thinking again about the landscape in Cornwall. The film's locations included Men-an-tol, Hell's Mouth cove and Madron Well in Cornwall. All the effects used were organically made. The music was composed by Peter Mackenzie of Cornish psych folk band Men-an-tol.

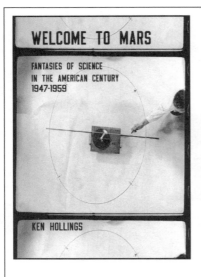

Welcome to Mars: Fantasies of Science in the American Century, 1947-1959

by Ken Hollings

312pp, pb, £11.99, illustrated, index
ISBN: 978095480548

'Welcome to Mars is a map of the post-war Zone, a non-fiction *Gravity's Rainbow* that follows the arc of Germany's V2 rocket to the end of the rainbow – to America.'
Erik Davis

Welcome To Mars draws upon newspaper accounts, advertising campaigns, declassified government archives, old movies and newsreels from this unique period when the future first took on a tangible presence. Ken Hollings depicts an unsettled time in which the layout of Suburbia reflected atomic bombing strategies, bankers and movie stars experimented with hallucinogens, brainwashing was just another form of interior decoration and strange lights in the sky were taken very seriously indeed.

Seamlessly interweaving developments in technology, popular culture, politics, changes in home life, the development of the self, collective fantasy and overwhelming paranoia, Hollings has produced an alarming and often hysterically funny vision of the past that would ultimately govern all of our futures.

'Ken Hollings shows brilliantly how the extraordinary web of technologies that drove the Cold War have shaped not just our culture but the very way we think of ourselves as human beings. Welcome to Mars offers a rare and fascinating glimpse of the roots of the strange humanoid culture we live in today.' *Adam Curtis*

Available now from *www.strangeattractor.co.uk*